CIRIA C644

BUILDING GREENer

Guidance on the use of green roofs, green walls and complementary features on buildings

J Newton Ecology Consultancy

D Gedge Livingroofs.org

P Early Livingroofs.org

S Wilson EPG

Coutesy G Kadas

sharing knowledge ■ building best practice

Classic House, 174–180 Old Street, London EC1V 9BP

TEL +44 (0)20 7549 3300 FAX 020 7253 0523

EMAIL enquiries@ciria.org WEBSITE www.ciria.org

Green roofs and walls are widely used in many countries to provide a range of benefits for the built environment. This guidance results from a comprehensive assessment of published information on green roofs and walls, and provides guidance on their design, construction and operation. The guide also describes how "quick wins" for biodiversity can be achieved in the built environment by incorporating nesting and roosting boxes for birds, bats and other animals.

BUILDING GREEN*er*

Guidance on the use of green roofs, green walls and complementary features on buildings

Newton, J; Gedge, D; Early, P; Wilson; S

CIRIA

C644 © CIRIA 2007 RP714 ISBN-13: 978-0-86017-644-2
ISBN-10: 0-86017-644-4

British Library Cataloguing in Publication Data

A catalogue record for this book is available from the British Library.

Keywords

Biodiversity, climate change, design and buildability, energy, land use planning, sustainable construction, urban drainage, urban regeneration

Reader interest	Classification	
Spatial planners, environmental regulators, clients, designers, architects, consulting engineers, contractors, facilities managers and those involved in developing the built environment	AVAILABILITY	Unrestricted
	CONTENT	Technical guidance
	STATUS	Committee-guided
	USER	Developers, planners, engineers

Published by CIRIA, Classic House, 174-180 Old Street, London, EC1V 9BP

ACKNOWLEDGEMENTS

Research contractor

This guidance is the outcome of CIRIA Research Project 714 *Biodiversity and buildings* and was jointly prepared by Ecology Consultancy Ltd., Livingroofs.org and EPG.

Authors

John Newton BSc MSc CEnv MIEEM

John Newton is managing director of Ecology Consultancy Ltd and environment director of Crane Environmental Ltd. An ecologist with more than 25 years experience, including work in the voluntary and private sectors, he has spent the last 15 years actively involved in working with the construction industry to improve its performance on ecological issues.

Dusty Gedge

Dusty Gedge is co-founder of Livingroofs.org, a not for profit organisation established to promote, advise upon and seek research into green roofs and similar structures within the context of urban and rural regeneration. He has been one of the most influential figures in promoting the use of green roofs in the UK and received the 2004 Andrew Lees Memorial Award in recognition of his work. He provides advice on green roof design to a wide variety of organisations including local authorities, consultants, contractors and green roof suppliers.

Paul Early BEng MSc AMImechE

Paul has 20 years of experience working in the engineering industry and has a specialisation in green roofs following the attainment of an MSc in advanced environmental and energy studies. He has supported Livingroof.org in its activities for the last two years and presented a green roof course for the *World green roof congress* in Basel, Switzerland in 2005.

Steve Wilson BEng MSc CEng CEnv CSci MICE MCIWEM FGS

Steve has over 20 years practical experience of geotechnical and environmental design for civil engineering and building structures including drainage design and redevelopment of contaminated land. He is co-author of CIRIA publication C582 *Source control using constructed pervious surfaces* (Pratt *et al*, 2002) and C609 *Sustainable drainage systems. Hydraulic, structural and water quality advice* (Wilson *et al*, 2004) He has spent the last five years promoting the use of SUDS and helping to develop innovative solutions to urban drainage problems.

Steering group

Following CIRIA's usual practice, the research project was guided by a Steering Group that comprised:

Members

Jean Venables (chair)	Crane Environmental Limited
Alan Bamforth	ABG Environmental Limited
Nick Cooper	Alderburgh Limited
Ian Johnston/Nick Ridout	Alumasc Exterior Building Products Limited
Paul Hinds	East of England Development Agency
David Knight/Peter Massini	Natural England
Steve Ball	English Partnerships
James Farrell/Sue Wolff	Greater London Authority
Mike Cottage	Greenfix Limited
Jon Atkinson	KBR
Mark Thompson	Knauf Insulation Limited
Sule Nisancioglu	London Borough of Haringey
Bronwen Fletcher	London Development Agency
Chris Mills	NHBC
Mathew Frith	Peabody Trust
Andrew Shuttleworth	SEL Environmental
Martin Bolton/Peter Wain	South East England Development Agency

CIRIA's project managers for the guidance were Mark Bentley and Paul Shaffer, with support from Jo Facer.

Project funders

The project was funded by the following organisations:

ABG Environmental Limited
Aldeburgh Limited
Alumasc Exterior Building Products Limited
East of England Development Agency
Natural England
English Partnerships
Environmental Protection Group Limited
Greater London Authority
Greenfix Limited
Kellogg Brown and Root
Knauf Insulation Limited
London Development Agency
NHBC
SEL Environmental
South East England Development Agency

Contributors

CIRIA gratefully acknowledges the support of the funding organisations and the technical advice and help provided by members of the Steering Group. The authors would also like to express special thanks to:

Gary Grant, Barry Nicholson, Derek Brown, Liz Greenhalgh, Claire Bennie, Yen Chit Chong (LBC), Ed Mayer (London's Swifts), Clare Darlaston Concern for Swifts (Scotland), John Goldsmith, Eddie Hughes (LBC), David DeRosa (EPG Clear), Cath Basilio (Sheffield City Council), Katie Parsons (Bat Conservation Trust) and to Jacklyn Johnston – who started the ball rolling with the inspiration to write **BUILDING GREEN**.

Courtesy G Kadas

Courtesy M Frith

CONTENTS

List of case studies

List of figures

List of tables

List of boxes

FOREWORD

BUILDING GREEN*er* is inspirational guidance that will without doubt move the incorporation of green roofs, green walls and other complementary features from the quirky to the mainstream by providing advice and guidance, and illustrated with practical examples. The guidance will be further illustrated and kept up-to-date in the associated website: <www.ciria.org/buildinggreener>.

As can be seen from the case studies, it is a solution increasingly being adopted worldwide to deal with common challenges of attenuating stormwater runoff, enhancing biodiversity, improving the aesthetics of buildings and reducing greenhouse gas emissions, especially in urban areas. Mayors of many cities are now promoting the concept of green roofs and are incorporating these ideas into their planning requirements.

All new buildings and structures could, and should, incorporate most of the features described in this guidance, and existing structures could be adapted in some way. It may lead to a reduction in energy use in the building and contribute to climate change adaptation.

Chairing the enthusiastic CIRIA Project Steering Group has been stimulating and the lessons we have all learnt from each other we want to share with you in this timely report. I would especially ask all clients commissioning buildings to follow this guidance now to make your vital contribution to managing climate change and improving the quality of life, not just for our benefit but also for the benefit of future generations.

Please read **BUILDING GREEN*er***, whether you are the client, designer, planner, contractor or facilities manager, and use it on your current and future projects to help us all meet the target of One Planet Living.

Jean Venables

Jean Venables OBE FREng FICE CEnv
Crane Environmental
Chair, Project Steering Group

A Introduction and background

A "modern" green roof in Rackwick Bay, Hoy, Orkney Islands (courtesy P Early)

1 INTRODUCTION TO THE GUIDANCE

1.1 What is the guidance about?

Have you ever discussed the benefits and pitfalls of green roofs, green walls or other features such as bat boxes, with clients, planners, contractors or consultants? Have you ever wondered what green roofs and walls are all about? Are you interested in sustainable development and environmental improvement? If the answer to any of these questions is yes, then this document will be of interest to you. It provides guidance on the use of green roofs, walls and complementary features in buildings to secure environmental advantage.

Green roofs are intentionally vegetated roofs, ie the roof is designed either to allow vegetation to colonise naturally or to be deliberately seeded or planted as part of the roof construction. Green walls have plants growing on them, or integrated within them. Nesting and roosting boxes, and similar features, provide easy and relatively cheap ways of enhancing the biodiversity interest of buildings.

Green roofs and walls can provide a number of other benefits in addition to biodiversity (Figure 1.1). This book provides detailed information on the essential design issues related to how all these features can be included within buildings and how to maximise environmental benefits.

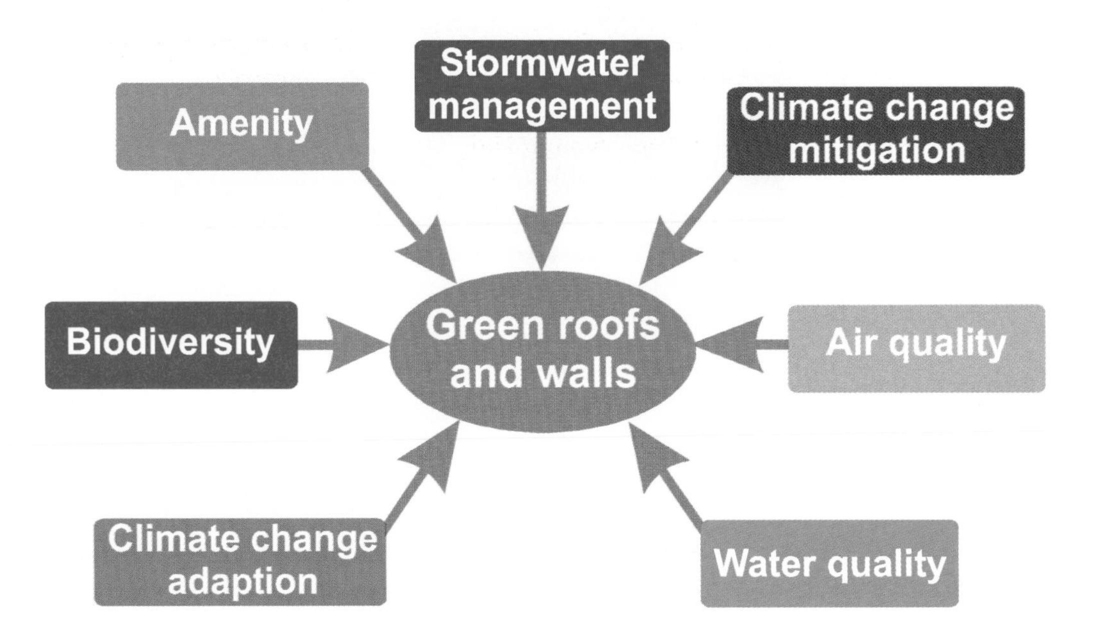

Figure 1.1 *Potential benefits of green roofs and walls*

1.2 The scope of the guidance

The guidance is intended for use by any professionals involved in the built environment who require independent information and guidance on the design, construction and maintenance of green roofs, green walls or complementary methods of enhancing biodiversity (eg nesting and roosting boxes). The contribution that green roofs and walls can make to biodiversity, stormwater management and climate change mitigation, and adaptation are explained in detail. The legislative and policy drivers that support such initiatives are covered, followed by guidance on the specification and construction of green roofs and walls. The guidance also describes how "quick wins" for biodiversity can be achieved by incorporating nesting and roosting boxes for birds, bats and other animals within the building fabric.

The contents of its various parts are described as follows:

Part A **Introduction and background** introduces the concept of green roofs, green walls and complementary features (eg nest boxes), and the role they can play in conserving and enhancing biodiversity, climate change mitigation and adaptation, and stormwater management. It also discusses relevant legislation, planning guidance, building regulations and supporting initiatives.

Part B **Green roofs** provides detailed information on green roofs including the potential benefits they offer to biodiversity, stormwater management and climate change mitigation and adaptation, and the key issues to be considered during their design, construction and maintenance. It also illustrates how the various methods discussed perform in practice by referring to test sites and case studies.

Part C **Green walls** provides a similar analysis to that for green roofs in Part B.

Part D **Nestboxes and other features** provides an introduction to the use of nestboxes, bat roosting boxes and similar features, on and within the fabric of buildings to secure important biodiversity enhancement for little cost or effort. Summary information is provided along with references to documents where more detailed guidance relating to specific species can be found.

Appendices provide detailed information and technical background to the issues covered in the guidance and a **Glossary** defines the terms used in the publication.

Finally, a full list of **References** is provided.

The following icons are used to identify particular subjects or information:

Case study/example

Regulation or policy

Cross reference to other important guidance

Introduction and background: Key points

- green roofs are intentionally vegetated roofs, with either naturally colonised or planted vegetation
- green walls have plants growing on them, or integrated within them
- green roofs and green walls can make significant contributions to the enhancement of biodiversity, stormwater amelioration and the climate mitigation, and adaptation
- there are other ways of enhancing the biodiversity of buildings, for example by providing nesting and roosting boxes.

2 BUILDING GREENER – THE OVERALL CONTEXT

2.1 The challenge – acceptance and integration

In the 21st century sustainable development is high on the national agenda. The UK Government has produced a number of initiatives that indicate its concern, not least its sustainable development strategy *Securing the Future* (Defra, 2005). This document sets out priorities for action which include climate change and energy conservation, and protection of natural resources and environmental enhancement (including specific reference to biodiversity). At the built environment level, the UK Government's strategy for more sustainable construction, *Building a Better Quality of Life* (DETR, 2000), identifies a number of themes which are of particular importance for the construction industry including:

- minimising energy use
- preserving and enhancing biodiversity
- conserving water resources.

The implementation of green roofs, green walls, and complementary features can contribute significantly to meeting the challenge of sustainable development by:

- providing engineered solutions to stormwater management
- contributing to climate change mitigation and adaptation
- providing a landscape that reflects local biodiversity and character.

Such an approach also brings with it wider environmental and social benefits. These benefits have been discussed by a number of authors (Johnston and Newton, 2004; Grant *et al*, 2003) and include:

- ecology and biodiversity – providing new wildlife habitat, mitigation for habitat lost through development, and providing green links or stepping stones for species movement through urban areas
- amenity – aesthetically more appealing than bare flat roofs, with the potential to provide amenity space for people in some cases
- health – provides psychological benefit associated with experiencing a green view and contact with nature, and physiological benefit through wider air quality improvements
- building fabric – protects the roof from harmful ultra violet radiation and mechanical damage. Reduces temperature range and its impacts on building materials
- economic – extends roof life; may reduce requirement for water storage and associated pipework; may reduce requirement for winter heating and summer cooling. In the case of extensive (see Section 5.4.3) green roofs, the use of recycled and reused materials help reduce overall costs
- environmental – help to reduce air pollution and noise.

To maximise the contribution that green roofs and walls can make towards sustainability objectives, these potential benefits need to be considered holistically. In a number of countries one of the major drivers for implementation of green roofs is the control of stormwater runoff. Until recently, this has led to a focus on systems that use plants which are known to absorb water quickly and hold it, such as *sedums spp*. These systems provide some intrinsic benefit to biodiversity, but this is limited by the lack of plant species variety. In response, a more holistic approach is being championed by the city authorities in Karlsruhe in Germany and Basel in Switzerland. This approach maintains the stormwater management performance, through the use of deeper substrates, while enhancing biodiversity through the use of local substrates and plant species.

In the ways outlined, green roofs, walls and complementary features can help to realise the aims and objectives of numerous government action plans and policies including those relating to the wider sustainable communities agenda. This is discussed in more detail in Chapter 3.

2.2 The importance of urban areas for biodiversity

Urban areas are important for wildlife. Gardens and green spaces have been shown to have high biodiversity even compared to many rural areas, and wasteland sites play host to rare plants and invertebrates. A bird that benefits from such habitats and is almost uniquely confined to urban areas in the UK, is the rare and specially protected black redstart *Phoenicurus ochruros*. Commonly found in rocky and craggy places elsewhere in Europe, it has made its home on abandoned inner city sites that to a certain extent mimic its natural habitat. Other species that have adapted to the urban environment include swifts *Apus apus*, grey heron *Ardea cinerea*, great spotted woodpecker *Dendrocopos major* and speckled wood butterfly *Pararge aegeria* (Defra, 2002).

However, characteristic "townies", such as house sparrow *Passer domesticus* and starling *Sturnus vulgaris*, have fared less well in recent years. Urban bat populations have also been reduced. For example, surveys of Greater London's bat populations have shown a statistically significant decline in numbers since the mid-1980s, particularly for the noctule, Leisler's and serotine bats. Leisler's and serotine are both species that roost regularly in buildings (Guest, Jones and Tovey, 2002).

Greenspace is now under greater threat as the Government seeks higher densities of development and the reuse of brownfield sites. The cycle of regeneration is now arguably more frantic than ever before. Old wasteland sites are being developed, and the sites that once would have formed new wastelands are being regenerated before they have a chance to acquire any biodiversity interest. This results in habitat for species such as black redstarts being lost. Buildings with clean architectural lines are now in vogue, so that the nooks and crannies where swifts and other forms of wildlife are able to find a toehold are limited on new buildings. The general move to tidy up the urban environment often means valuable habitat and wildlife is removed.

In order to retain and enhance biodiversity interest, the variety and matrix of habitats that have typified our urban areas in the past need to be conserved and recreated. Gardens and greenspaces will always make a valuable contribution, but the more spontaneous wildlife habitats, no matter how small or apparently insignificant, also need to be considered. Considerable areas of flat roof exist in our urban areas in the case of the City of London 16 per cent of the surface area (Grant *et al*, 2003) which are in a sense wasted space serving little purpose for man or nature. The potential to convert these into a useful wildlife resource is enormous, as demonstrated in other countries such as Switzerland and Germany.

Some people will argue that wildlife does not have a place in an urban area, and belongs in the countryside. However, this discounts the fact that wildlife makes no value judgement on the places where it chooses to live – if the habitat is suitable then it is irrelevant whether it is town or country. Our quality of life is enhanced by contact with nature; people like to look out on to green vistas, as testified by the prices of property with such a view; the sound of bird song or the glimpse of a butterfly can help lift the spirit; and the canopy of trees can shelter us from the vagaries of the weather. With the current trend for increasing development density, the use of buildings to provide biodiversity benefits will become more important.

In general terms nature can contribute to our quality of life in four main ways (Grant *et al*, 2003):

1. **Appreciation** – nature for enjoyment, health and spiritual enrichment, a better living environment, cultural meaning and artistic inspiration.
2. **Knowledge** – a knowledge resource for general education, scientific and historic discovery, and environmental monitoring.
3. **Products** – sustainably harvested products such as food, fuel, medicines, cosmetics and construction materials.
4. **Ecosystem services** – natural systems provide basic life-support structures, without which our lives would be impossible or very costly to sustain. Our air, soils and climate are maintained by natural processes. Managed wisely, natural habitats can mitigate the effects of flooding and pollution.

Building biodiversity interest into the urban fabric has the potential to not only help conserve species of plant and animal, but also to contribute to our own quality of life and standard of living. It is not about allowing wildlife in all its diversity to have free rein over our living and working environment. It is about making use of buildings to provide structures and habitat where important species can survive without them necessarily having an impact on our lives, save for the benefit of enjoying their presence. It is also about using green roofs and walls, nest boxes and other features as part of a wider strategy of conserving and enhancing urban greenspace – a strategy that includes parks, gardens, and urban wildspace.

With careful planning, construction and management, buildings can help to retain and enhance the biodiversity of urban areas to the benefit of people and the wider environment. These benefits are discussed in more detail in Chapters 6 and 12.

2.3 The importance of stormwater management in urban areas

When a site is developed, impermeable surfaces and artificial piped-drainage systems are introduced. As a result, natural drainage patterns are disrupted and surface water runoff increases, with a resulting increase in downstream flood risk (Figure 2.1). Green roofs can help prevent this happening and should be used where possible as a source control technique within a well designed sustainable drainage system (SUDS).

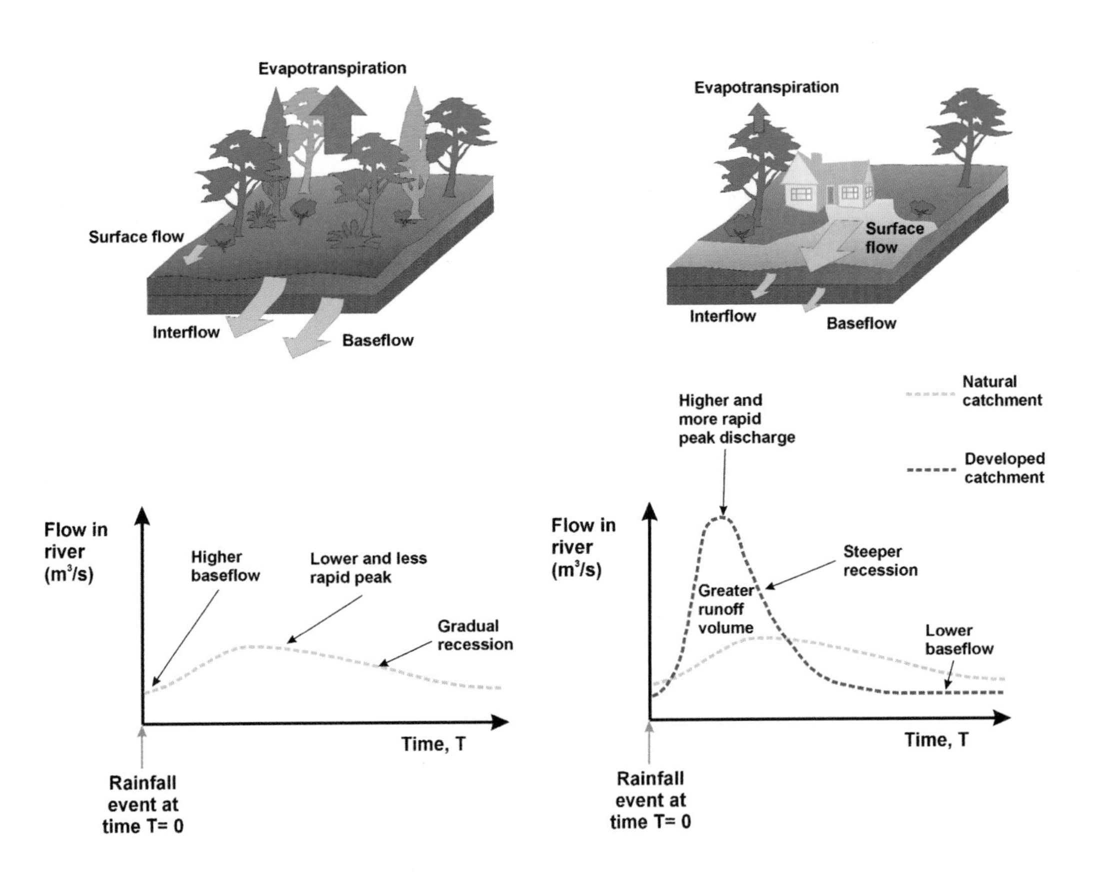

Figure 2.1 *Impact of development on stormwater runoff*

In the past, surface water drainage has been designed with the sole aim of reducing the risk of individual sites flooding from local rainfall. This required rainwater to be removed from sites as quickly as possible, typically via pipes to streams and rivers. There was little concern about the impact of site drainage on the wider environment. As development has increased, this historical approach to stormwater management has caused problems with flooding and diffuse pollution.

Recently sustainable drainage has been promoted to alleviate the problems associated with conventional drainage. The SUDS philosophy is to replicate the natural drainage patterns as closely as possible, and thereby reduce the impact of the development on the water environment. Controlling runoff, especially in urban areas where historically hard impermeable areas have reduced infiltration and percolation of water into the soil, is becoming increasingly important (CIRIA, 2007).

Green roofs have the potential to store rainwater in their substrate and, to a lesser extent, in and on the plants that grow on them, before it is evaporated or transpired back into the atmosphere. The amount of water that is stored and evaporated back will largely depend on the growing medium, its depth, and the type of plants used. Because of this water storage capability, the total volume of rainfall running off a green roof is significantly reduced when compared to conventional roofs (Figure 2.2). The precise reduction in runoff varies, and is dependent on a number of factors including the roof construction make up, season and rainfall patterns (see Appendix 3 for more details). Peak flow rates from green roofs are also reduced.

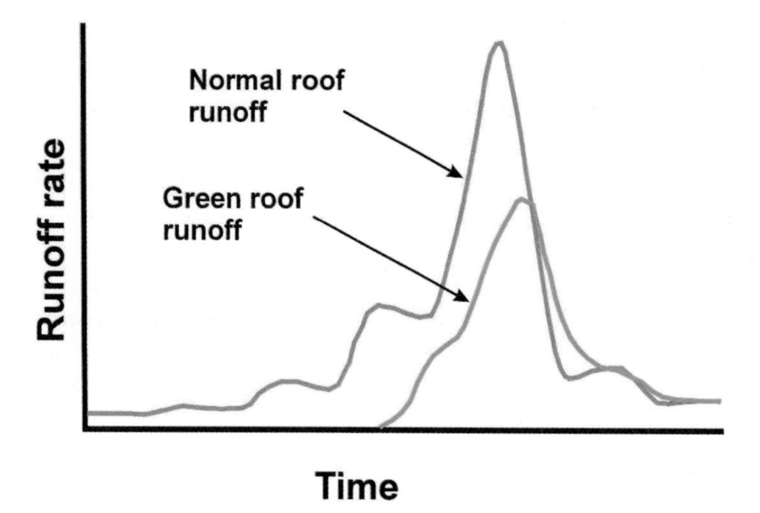

Figure 2.2 *Example comparison of runoff from green and conventional roofs*

As a result of the reduction in volumes and peak rates of runoff, green roofs can help to reduce flood risk in downstream watercourses and sewers. They have been used on a school in Sheffield to manage stormwater to meet the requirements of planning conditions (see Chapter 7). In Germany the contribution that green roofs can make to the management of stormwater runoff is one of the main reasons for their use (Grant *et al*, 2003).

Detailed studies that demonstrate the effective performance of green roofs in relation to stormwater management are provided in Appendix 3. An example is a study in Portland, Oregon, USA (an area that has a similar temperate climate and similar average rainfall conditions to the UK) that has shown green roofs should be able to retain about 65 to 100 per cent of the total volume of rainfall in summer, and in winter about 10 to 35 per cent. Peaks in the runoff rate were reduced for all storms (Liptan and Strecker, 2003). Further information on the performance of green roofs in stormwater management is provided in Chapter 7. Even during high intensity and prolonged rainfall, green roofs reduce and delay runoff although to a lesser extent than under more normal conditions. They do this by increasing the time of entry and time of concentration of the roof runoff.

The contribution that green roofs can make extends beyond stormwater volume management. Rainwater that runs off traditional roofs can contain pollutants (bird droppings or atmospheric pollution) that can harm the flora and fauna of aquatic ecosystems. Green roofs retain and bind contaminants and can therefore contribute to pollution removal from runoff. In Portland, Oregon, green roof policies are being driven by concerns about stormwater runoff and its impacts on river water quality and consequently salmon (Frerichs, 2002).

2.4 The importance of climate change mitigation and adaptation

Buildings being constructed today will have to accommodate possible climate change impacts over their lifetimes. Likewise, existing buildings will need to be adapted to allow for forecast climate change. An overview of the likely effects of climate change upon the roof is summarised below (BRE, 2004):

- faster aging and deterioration of polymer roof materials
- higher thermal movement of waterproof layer
- higher surface temperatures
- possible reduction of snow loads
- increased risk of water percolation into building components and materials

- increased subsidence and heave
- effect upon roof ventilation
- increase in frequency and duration of severe stormwater events and their runoff.

The "greening" of buildings as described in this guidance could potentially play a significant role in improving the climate change mitigation of buildings, and adaptation of existing buildings, to meet the demands imposed on them by climate change.

Two of the main benefits of green roofs and walls are the evaporative cooling effects and the albedo effect, which can reduce the cooling load on buildings during summer. Another benefit is the insulating effect of a green roof, especially on older, poorly insulated buildings. Green walls can also provide shading to glazed areas.

2.4.1 Green roofs and energy transfer

The insulating effect of a green roof can help reduce the transfer of heat between the external and internal environment or vice versa. This reduces internal heating and cooling costs, and prolongs the life of water proofing membranes. Research by Nottingham Trent University in the UK has shown that, during winter, roof membrane temperatures are significantly different between standard and green roofs (Table 2.1).

Table 2.1 *Comparison of waterproof membrane temperatures (data provided by Nottingham Trent University)*

Season	Mean air temperature	Temperature under membrane Standard roof	Temperature under membrane Green roof
Winter	0°C	0.2°C	4.7°C
Summer	18.4°C	32°C	17.1°C

The ability of the roof to act in this way is partially dependent on the amount of water held within plants and the substrate. Water retention can increase the amount of heat lost and therefore any efficiency gains largely depend on daily conditions. Accurate figures on the net effect of green roofs on energy efficiency during the winter months are, therefore, difficult to estimate.

In summer, poorly insulated roofs can lead to substantial overheating of the space beneath them, and this often results in an increased need for energy intensive air-conditioning. A green roof not only acts as an insulation barrier and provides thermal mass, but the combination of plant processes (photosynthesis and evapotranspiration) reduces the amount of solar energy absorbed by the roof membrane, thus leading to cooler temperatures beneath the surface.

If, as predicted, both average and extremes of temperature increase in the UK due to climate change, then the surface temperature of roofs and the effect this has on building performance will become an increasing concern. Many existing roofs are likely to be too poorly insulated to contend with these increases in temperature. Green roofs offer an important mechanism for providing extra insulation to adapt buildings to deal with the effects of climate change.

Green roofs complement the addition of conventional insulation to a new or refurbished building, particularly by being used as the ballast for inverted roofs as a replacement for conventional gravel or paving slabs. The refurbishment of a conventional flat roof is the ideal time to consider the cost-effective inclusion of a green roof to provide greater insulation, providing that the roof structure can support the weight of the new green roof.

Case study 1 City of Toronto – energy savings

A recent study in Toronto estimated that direct energy savings from reduced energy for cooling in the city would be $21 million a year, equivalent to 4.15 KWh/m² per year, if a city wide implementation of green roofs was carried out. Direct savings are a result of improved heat flow characteristics through the building envelope. The city-wide benefits were calculated based on the assumption that 100 per cent of available green roof area is used. The available green roof area included flat roofs on buildings with more than 350 sq m of roof area, and assumed at least 75 per cent of the roof area would be greened. The total available green roof area city-wide was determined to be 5000 hectares.

The demand reduction (based on peak demand reduction of 0.0023 kW per sq m) for city-wide green roof implementation, would be 114.6 MW. The cost of bringing in new generation capacity was estimated to be $600 000 per MW (based on a cost of building a new power plant estimated at $1.5 billion). Therefore the cost avoided from reduction in peak demand was estimated to be $68.7 million.

<www.toronto.ca/greenroofs> (Banting *et al*, 2005).

2.4.2 Green walls and surface temperature

During the summer, green walls act in much the same way as green roofs by reducing the surface temperature of the conventional wall through evapotranspiration and shading. Systems that use irrigation and hydroponic techniques provide additional benefit due to the cooling effect of evaporated water.

The purposeful shading of windows or "bioshading" has the potential to significantly reduce overheating due to internal solar gains in the summer, while allowing daylight into buildings during the winter. This will reduce the cooling load on the building.

Green walls can provide a greater barrier to wind, rain and snow during the winter months thus increasing the surface temperature of walls, with the main benefit being achieved by protecting the wall surface from the "wind chill" effect (although this effect is marginal if the wall is well insulated). Those systems that are separated from the wall surface by an air gap are likely to provide greater thermal insulation during the winter.

2.4.3 The urban heat island effect

The reduction in roof and wall surface temperature is important to the urban heat island effect and climate change adaptability. Temperatures in UK cities are greater than in surrounding suburban and rural areas as a result of many factors, such as the adsorption of solar radiation by conventional roofs and walls. The higher ambient temperatures resulting from climate change are predicted to increase the urban heat island effect further. Air pollution and smog are likely to increase for similar reasons.

Adapting buildings to reduce the surface temperature at roof and wall surfaces through the use of green roofs and walls will reduce a building's impact on the urban heat island effect. The more roof and wall space that can be used in this way, the more significant its impact on the urban heat island will be.

A study in Toronto (Banting *et al*, 2005) modelled the effect of green roofs on the city's urban heat island concluded that widespread greening of roofs would reduce local ambient temperature by between 0.5°C and 2°C. It was calculated that this could lead to city-wide indirect savings from reduced energy demand for cooling of $12 million, equivalent to 2.37 kWh/m² per year. Indirect savings are due to reduced temperature differences through the roofs and walls of buildings. The reduction in energy requirements was estimated to reduce carbon dioxide emissions from power stations by 32 200 tonnes per year.

2.5 Regionality

When installing a green roof for biodiversity or stormwater management benefit, it is important that consideration is given as to where in the UK the green roof is to be situated. For example, the climate in the south-east of England is very different to that on the west coast of Scotland, and what works for biodiversity in London may not work in Glasgow (and vice versa).

Wherever possible the "local distinctiveness" of a place, especially in terms of habitats or species, should be reflected in the materials that are used to create the green roof substrate, and the plants that are sown on or planted in to it. In other words, if the development is situated in a part of the country where chalk grassland is an important habitat, using calcareous material on a roof to try to replicate some of the qualities of that habitat makes sense. If seeding is required, then clearly a chalk grassland seed mix would be appropriate. Likewise while it may be of interest to try to attract some rare invertebrates to a roof there is no use attempting to do that if they are only found in south Essex and the building you are working on is in Manchester. Such local considerations are also referred to in PPS 3 Housing (see Appendix 1) in relation to the design of housing developments.

The precise location and orientation of the green roof or wall that is to be installed should be considered at the planning stage. Careful consideration of micro-climate and orientation could potentially make the difference between a successful project and a complete disaster. For example, in major urban centres, overshadowing, reflected radiation, and increased wind velocities could all have an important role in determining whether or not a project is successful.

Ecologists should always be commissioned to advise on what habitat and species are appropriate for a particular roof. They should study the local ecology and identify the conservation priorities. Local biodiversity action plans (BAP) provide useful information as to what is seen to be important in the regional and local contexts. Wherever possible, green roofs and walls should respond to local BAP targets to ensure that they make a positive wildlife contribution.

Regionality is also a consideration in maximising the stormwater management benefits of green roofs and walls and designing them for climate change adaptation and mitigation. Once again, to use examples from south-east and north-west England, Essex is dry and in the summer can be quite hot, whereas Manchester experiences much more rainfall and does not achieve such high temperatures as regularly. Therefore in Manchester the green roof design may require a thicker substrate to achieve the same degree of runoff volume reduction as a green roof in Essex. Consideration of local ambient temperature and rainfall patterns, and issues such as local flood control requirements, will need to be considered early in the design stage, alongside regional biodiversity aspects, if a green roof is to be successful in meeting expectations.

Building greener – the overall context: Key points

- an holistic approach to the design of green roofs, green walls and complementary features on buildings will enable solutions to be provided that can contribute to a wide range of sustainable development objectives, including stormwater management, climate change mitigation and adaptation, and the conservation and enhancement of biodiversity
- urban areas are important for wildlife. In order to retain and enhance biodiversity interest a variety and matrix of habitats need to be conserved, enhanced and created. The use of green roofs can play an important part in this, providing valuable habitat for a variety of species
- building biodiversity interest into our urban fabric has the potential to not only help conserve important species of plant and animal, but also to contribute to our own quality of life and standard of living
- green roofs reduce the volume and rate of rainwater runoff and can be used as a source control technique within a well designed sustainable drainage system (SUDS). The design will require consideration of local rainfall patterns and issues such as local flood control requirements
- runoff from traditional roofs can contain pollutants (bird droppings or atmospheric pollution) that can harm the flora and fauna of aquatic ecosystems. Green roofs retain and bind contaminants and can therefore contribute to pollution removal from runoff
- buildings in construction today will have to accommodate likely climate change impacts over their lifetimes. The "greening" of buildings described in this guide could potentially play a significant role in achieving this
- green roofs and walls can improve the thermal performance of a building through shading and increased thermal mass in the summer, sheltering in the winter and improved thermal resistance throughout the year
- when installing a green roof it is important to consider:
  - the regional climate (temperature and rainfall patterns)
  - the micro climate and orientation of the roof
  - local habitats and species (particularly those addressed in local BAP targets)
  - local flood control objectives
- wherever possible, local habitats and species should be reflected in the type of substrate used and the plants that are sown on, or planted into, it
- ecologists should always be commissioned to advise on what habitat and species are appropriate for a particular roof or wall in order to meet local BAP targets.

3 POLICY CONTEXT

3.1 Legislation and guidance

Wildlife in the UK is protected largely by a handful of Acts and Regulations, although there is a host of other legislation that can influence what happens to our wild flora and fauna (Newton *et al*, 2004). There is no legislation that states that wildlife should be protected on roofs or walls or that encourages green roofs or walls *per se*. However, the principal piece of wildlife legislation in the UK, the Wildlife and Countryside Act 1981 (as amended) (WCA, 1981)[1] does provide, among other things, varying degrees of protection to a wide variety of plants and animals some of which will occur, nest or roost on or within buildings. For example, all wild birds are protected by the Act as are their nests. The most rare and vulnerable bird species, including species found in urban areas such as the black redstart and peregrine falcon, are in Schedule 1 of the Act, which makes it an offence to disturb these species while they are nest building, or at a nest containing eggs or young, or to disturb the dependent young of such a bird.

3.1.1 Wildlife protection

All species of bat in Britain are protected by the Wildlife and Countryside Act (WCA, 1981). Importantly in England and Wales the WCA 1981 was amended by the Countryside and Rights of Way Act 2000 (CRoW, 2000) with the effect that reckless disturbance of any bat or damage or destruction of its place of shelter became an offence. Since this is easier to prove in Court than just intentional disturbance the law is now stronger. Similar protection under CRoW (2000) is afforded to nesting birds. Bats are also recognised as European Protected Species under EC Directive 92/43/EEC ("the Habitats Directive").

From the point of view of buildings and biodiversity, this legislation means that any works that may impact on nesting birds or roosting bats needs very careful consideration. Mitigation for the loss of nesting or roosting habitat may be required. In the case of bats, if there is a roost in the fabric of a building, a license will have to be obtained from the Department for Environment Food and Rural Affairs (Defra) in England, (Scottish Executive Environment and Rural Affairs Department (SEERAD) in Scotland, the Welsh Assembly, or the Environment and Heritage Service – Natural Heritage in Northern Ireland) before any redevelopment of the site can take place. Full mitigation for the loss of any bat roost will be required in order to conserve the species "favourable conservation status" (Scottish Natural Heritage, 2003).

While legislation is good at protecting nesting and roosting habitat, it often fails to protect the important foraging habitat on which birds and other animals depend. For example, although the availability of suitable nesting habitat for black redstarts is undoubtedly a limiting factor, the loss of foraging habitat is arguably of greater concern (Frith and Gedge, 2000). The loss of brownfield and other urban wasteland areas means that no matter how much the nesting requirements are taken into account in development, black redstarts will not be able to survive. Black redstarts are one bird species in particular that can benefit enormously by the provision of green roofs.

While there may not be any direct legal requirement to provide green roofs, walls or other structures for wildlife, they may be seen as mitigation for the impacts of habitat loss affecting legally protected or BAP priority species. The government is keen to see "greening" of

---

1 The laws referenced in the guide generally refer to the situation in England and Wales. The other countries that make up the UK – Northern Ireland and Scotland – may have different laws to those of England and Wales, but their aims are broadly similar.

residential developments (for example in PPG 3 – see Appendix 1) and green roofs, green walls and complementary features can provide a valuable contribution to this goal.

3.1.2 The Water Framework Directive

The Water Framework Directive (2000/60/EC) was transposed into UK national legislation in December 2003. The Directive takes account of all the different objectives for which the aquatic environment is protected (ecology, drinking water, health and particular habitats), and requires that measures taken to achieve the objectives are coordinated properly.

The Water Framework Directive encourages a more sustainable approach to water management by:

- establishing an holistic approach to managing the water environment, based on river basins, integrating water quantity with quality considerations
- establishing quality objectives for all water bodies in order to achieve good status
- establishing a quality classification system for surface and groundwater that includes chemical, hydromorphological and ecological parameters
- establishing statutory controls in relation to pollution of water bodies from point and diffuse sources to prevent deterioration in the status of water bodies
- achieving environmental objectives in a cost-effective way.

A specific condition is the requirement for the control of surface water discharges. This means that all discharges of urban runoff may have to be managed such that their impact on the receiving environment is mitigated. This may effectively preclude the use of the traditional approach to drainage and will require the SUDS philosophy to be adopted to reduce the volume and rate of runoff, and to remove pollution. Green roofs are ideal to help meet these requirements.

3.2 Planning policy framework

The planning policy framework provides broad guidance in respect of, among other things, biodiversity, sustainable drainage and thermal efficiency. It tends not to be prescriptive (eg a developer will construct X sq m of green roof or achieve Y kg/m^2 of CO_2), but rather focuses on developing a framework that results in appropriate planning decisions being made at the strategic, local or site levels. In this respect guidance exists at a variety of levels including national, regional and local.

At a national level in England, Planning Policy Statement 9 (PPS9) *Biodiversity and Geological Conservation* is an important tool in reviewing the proposed impacts of a development. One of its key principles is that...*"the aim of planning decisions should be to prevent harm to biodiversity and geological conservation interests"* (see Appendix 1). It also identifies that local authorities should take measures to protect the habitats of species of importance for the conservation of biodiversity, and to refuse permission where harm to the species or their habitats may occur, unless the benefits and needs of the development outweight any harm. Species of principal importance are defined under Section 74 of CRoW 2000 and include a variety of plant, bird and invertebrate species as well as six species of bat.

While PPS9 focuses largely on the protection of statutory and non statutory designated wildlife sites, it also seeks to strengthen the protection given to networks of habitat, for example wastelands, woodlands and grasslands, including those within urban areas.

Other Planning Policy Statements also provide support to the inclusion of green roofs and walls within the development. (**Note:** PPSs may take a different form with different names in Northern

Ireland, Scotland and Wales):

- PPS25 (*Development and Flood Risk*) advises that restriction and reduction of surface water runoff can be encouraged by the provision of sustainable drainage systems (SUDS)
- PPS3 (*Housing*). The aim of this guidance "*...is that the planning system is used to its maximum effect to ensure the delivery of decent homes that are well-designed, make best use of land, are energy efficient, make the most of new building technologies and help to deliver sustainable development*"
- PPS1 (*Delivering Sustainable Development – General Policy and Principles*). Incorporating biodiversity, SUDS and thermal efficiency into buildings is in agreement with many of the aims of this guidance.

SUDS are promoted as the preferred drainage option by the following national planning policies:

- England PPS25: *Development and Flood Risk* (2006)
- Scotland SPP7: *Planning and Flooding* (January 2004)
- Wales TAN15: *Development and Flood Risk* (July 2004)
- Northern Ireland PPS15: *Planning and Flood Risk* (2004).

As discussed in Section 2.3, green roofs can be considered as an important source control method, which is a fundamental consideration for SUDS.

Further information regarding the relevant parts of these planning policy statements is provided in Appendix 1.

Policies reflecting this guidance are incorporated into development plans or frameworks at the regional and local level. For instance Lewisham Council's revised unitary development plan (UDP) (London Borough of Lewisham, 2002) contains a green roof policy. A number of local authorities are also preparing supplementary planning documents (SPD's – formerly supplementary planning guidance or SPG) on sustainable building, to address issues such as thermal efficiency, energy and water use, and sustainable drainage. In London, Westminster City's Sustainable Building SPG (City of Westminster, 2003) makes specific reference to green roofs. The Corporation of London along with the British Council for Offices has prepared a research advice note on green roofs in order to introduce planners, developers, architects and facilities managers to the concept (BCO, 2003). Haringey Council has produced a guide entitled *Greening Your Home* aimed at local householders which includes guidance on green roofs and SUDS.

It is clear that the continuing review and revision of planning policy guidance is beginning to take greater account of sustainable development principles. The provision of green roofs and walls, and the potential benefits they bring for biodiversity, stormwater management and thermal efficiency are likely to prove an increasingly important means of delivering these policies in the near future.

3.3 Biodiversity action planning

At the 1992 UNCED conference in Rio, the UK Government signed up to the Convention on Biological Diversity and as a result produced *Biodiversity: The UK Action Plan* (Department of the Environment, 1994). Since that time, biodiversity action plans (BAP) have been produced at all levels; national, regional and local, and even at the company or organisation level eg Highways Agency. These plans are intended as a guide to the priorities for wildlife conservation, the action that needs to be taken and the resources that will be required. In the London BAP (LBP, 2006), urban wasteland is subject to an action plan, and in regard to species there are action plans for bats, black redstarts, peregrine falcons, house sparrows, and stag beetles among others – all species that can benefit from the greening of buildings.

The Corporation of London BAP (Corporation of London, 2003) identifies vertical habitats as being important to biodiversity and includes a vertical habitat action plan in order to promote their establishment and management, and to encourage their inclusion in new development. Key actions in the plan include:

- encouraging and grant aiding the erection of nest boxes at selected sites in the City
- creating new green roofs to demonstrate good design and best practice.

The Corporation of London BAP also has action plans for peregrine falcon, house sparrow and black redstart.

Elsewhere in Britain, the Birmingham and the Black Country BAP (The Wildlife Trust for Birmingham and the Black Country, 2000) also lists black redstarts as a priority species, and the Newcastle BAP (Newcastle City Council, 2001) includes a target to install nest boxes on 50 per cent of suitable buildings by 2006 and on 100 per cent by 2010.

The Lancashire BAP (LBAP, 2006) includes the objective:

- to assess, manage and promote biodiversity in new and existing built structures throughout Lancashire.

Biodiversity action plans can translate into planning policy in various ways. For example, the London Borough of Westminster state in their unitary development plan (pre-inquiry draft) that *"developers will have to demonstrate that their proposals would either preserve or enhance the habitats and species protected in the Westminster and the National and London biodiversity action plans"* (Policy ENV 15). As noted in Section 3.2, species of principal importance for biodiversity are now material considerations in the planning process.

3.4 Building Regulations and Standards

The UK Building Regulations contain no direct reference to green roofs, only to the general standards of roof construction. Green roofs can be constructed to meet these standards. There are not, as yet, any other British industry standards to which a designer may refer. There is reference to green roofs, but no design guidance, in BS EN 12056:2000 *Gravity Drainage Systems inside buildings Part 3 roof drainage layout and calculation*. Green roofs can be designed to meet this standard.

Part L of the Building Regulations (updated in 2006) aims to substantially increase the energy efficiency of new and existing buildings in a variety of ways including higher standards of insulation. Green roofs and walls can make a contribution towards increased insulation, especially where retrofitted on to buildings with insulation levels that do not meet the new standards.

Local authorities still require guidance on green roofs and green walls in order to ensure that the correct decisions are being made, and that appropriate designs are recommended by developers and their designers. At present, manufacturers and consultants supply this information as circumstances dictate.

Some manufacturers are concerned that this lack of a formal standard is allowing sub-standard systems to be installed at a cheaper cost, with the danger that their reputation and that of green roofs will be damaged. In the absence of any British Standards, most designers, manufacturers and installers are currently relying on using the German Landscape Development Research

Society (FLL) guidelines for the design and construction of green roofs (FLL, 2002).

3.5 Other initiatives

Other areas of social and planning policy support consideration of green roofs and walls through, for example, the importance of providing quality public space. However, there is no detailed policy that directly promotes the application of green roofs or walls.

Currently government priorities for "livability" are to:

- create attractive and welcoming parks, play areas and public spaces
- improve the physical structure of places
- make places cleaner and maintain them better
- improve people's views of the quality of their local environment.

Case study 2 Parkside Community Technology College, Plymouth, UK

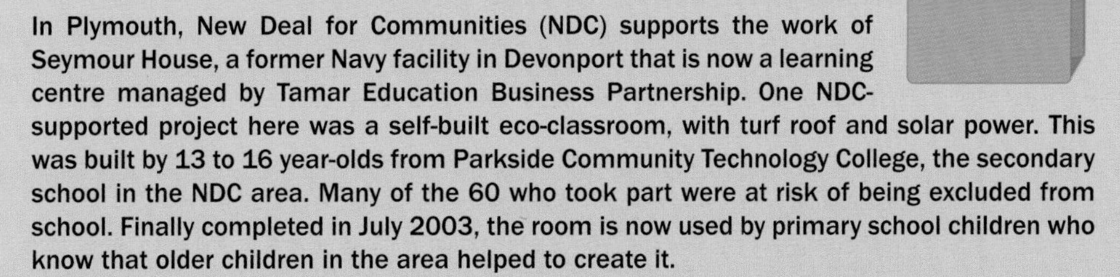

In Plymouth, New Deal for Communities (NDC) supports the work of Seymour House, a former Navy facility in Devonport that is now a learning centre managed by Tamar Education Business Partnership. One NDC-supported project here was a self-built eco-classroom, with turf roof and solar power. This was built by 13 to 16 year-olds from Parkside Community Technology College, the secondary school in the NDC area. Many of the 60 who took part were at risk of being excluded from school. Finally completed in July 2003, the room is now used by primary school children who know that older children in the area helped to create it.

***Making it happen in neighbourhoods. The national strategy for neighbourhood renewal – four years on* (Office of the Deputy Prime Minister, 2005).**

These priorities are enshrined in a raft of guidance and policy, the intention of which is to lift the social and environmental quality of urban living.

Within the construction industry a variety of environmental assessment tools exist that can indirectly promote the use of green roof and wall technology. These include BREEAM, CEEQUAL and NEAT.

BREEAM (Building Research Establishment Environmental Assessment Method) is a means of reviewing and improving the environmental performance of various types of buildings. Among the criteria that are used to assess the potential environmental impact of a building are those that consider site ecology. Credits can be achieved for minimising ecological damage, for designing in positive enhancement of site ecology and for protecting existing features.

EcoHomes is the version of BREEAM that is used for assessing new homes. Its 2006 edition provides the opportunity to gain credits by incorporating rainwater holding facilities and/or sustainable drainage techniques including green roofs, biodiversity enhancements, and features that minimise emissions of carbon dioxide to the atmosphere arising from the operation of a home and its services. All public funded housing from 2006 has to achieve EcoHomes very good rating; green roofs and walls could make a valuable contribution towards realising this. EcoHomes is also becoming embraced and eventually will be replaced by the DCLG's *Code for Sustainable Homes*.

CEEQUAL (Civil Engineering Environmental Quality Assessment and Award Scheme) rewards high environmental quality in civil engineering projects. Ecology is one of 12 criteria used to assess a project. Credits are given for best practice in respect of a range of issues including legal compliance, conservation and enhancement of biodiversity, habitat creation measures, and monitoring and maintenance.

NEAT (NHS Environmental Assessment Tool) – NHS Estates has developed a self assessment scheme called NEAT. The aim of NEAT is to raise awareness of the impacts that NHS facilities and services can have on the environment and to estimate the level of environmental impact taking place. There is a focus on patient well-being and the positive effects that a green outlook can have on recovering good health. NHS Estates have their own design indicators and at the Norfolk and Norwich University Hospital use has been made of gardens and courtyards to improve the space and make better use of sunlight. Green roofs and walls and the use of nest boxes could make a similar positive contribution.

Policy context: Key points

- the main legislation is the Wildlife and Countryside Act (WCA) 1981, although there is a host of other legislation that potentially can influence what happens to our wild flora and fauna
- any works that may impact on nesting birds or roosting bats need very careful consideration. Mitigation for the loss of nesting or roosting habitat may be required
- protecting the foraging habitat on which birds and other animals depend is important and can be achieved by the provision of green roofs and walls
- in general, the planning policy framework provides broad guidance in respect of biodiversity, sustainable drainage and thermal efficiency. Some of the key documents (in England and Wales) in relation to green roof and wall benefits are PPS9 *Biodiversity and Geological Conservation*, PPS25 *Development and Flood Risk* and PPS1 *General Policy and Principles*
- a number of local authorities have supplementary planning documents on sustainable building, to address issues such energy efficiency, biodiversity and sustainable drainage
- biodiversity action plans (BAP) have been produced at all levels: national, regional, local and at the company or organisation level. These plans provide a guide to the priorities for wildlife conservation, the action that needs to be taken and the resources that will be required. They should be considered when planning and designing green roofs and walls
- green roofs and walls could potentially make contribution to the increased insulation and energy efficiency requirements of Part L of the Building Regulations, especially where retrofitted on to buildings with insulation levels that do not meet the new standards
- green roofs can be considered as an important SUDS source control method. They can help to achieve the aims of the various planning documents relating to stormwater management (PPS25, SPP7, TAN 15 and PPS15)
- the Water Framework Directive requires that measures are taken to manage the water environment and achieve good quality status. A specific condition is the requirement for the control of surface water discharges. Green roofs are ideal to help meet these requirements
- green roofs can be constructed to meet UK Building Regulations. However, there are not as yet any specific UK industry standards for green roofs to which designers can refer.

4 CONSTRUCTION AND DEVELOPMENT CONTEXT

4.1 Critical issues for construction and operation

The provision of green roofs and walls is often constrained by concerns at the design stage regarding structural issues, maintenance requirements and potential damage to the building fabric during its lifetime. In some cases these may be justified, but in most they are not. There are potential advantages during operation that may be overlooked and there are benefits during construction that may not be registered at the design stage.

In this section the development and construction cycle is reviewed, to provide an overview of the advantages and disadvantages at each stage, and an insight into the challenges and opportunities that need to be considered early in the design process.

4.1.1 Planning/design

Clients and designers often focus on appearance and maintenance issues so many of the benefits that green roofs can bring to a project are not always recognised at the design stage. Proprietary systems such as sedum matting are often specified because they appear to provide an easy solution. Unfortunately, this can result in more naturalistic systems that may provide greater environmental advantage being overlooked because they are perceived as being less predictable.

Similarly, some of the challenges of managing green roofs for maintenance or access are not considered early enough in the construction cycle. For example, using sedum matting can lead to maintenance requirements that a building service manager may eventually decide to forego (weeding etc). Assurances regarding high standards of appearance gained at the design stage can lead to high start up costs, and may then be made redundant by lack of maintenance. Designers should design a green roof or wall for ease of maintenance.

A carefully designed and constructed bespoke roof can offer many advantages over its proprietary counterpart. These can include:

- lower construction costs (for example by using site-won crushed concrete or brick as substrate)
- site specific design to suit a required maintenance regime
- site specific choice of fauna to reduce maintenance requirements, minimise risk of plants dying and to maximise biodiversity provision to suit local needs
- design of specific areas that are overlooked for maximum aesthetic benefits (appearance is usually not a concern in areas that are not overlooked).

Green walls are generally designed on a bespoke basis to meet site specific criteria. See Parts B and C for further information.

4.1.2 Construction

Green roofs can be beneficial during construction, as once installed they can protect the water proofing from on-going works. Protecting the vegetation from construction activities will have to be considered.

Critical issues that need to be managed during construction of green roofs and walls include:

- health and safety (working at height is one of the most dangerous construction operations)
- how materials will be transported to the roof
- impact on programme of planting requirements (eg if planting needs to be undertaken in a specific season)
- requirements for temporary protection works or support.

Further information is provided in Parts B and C.

4.1.3 Operation

The advantages of green roofs and green walls during the life of the building are not merely related to thermal efficiency, stormwater management and biodiversity. Green roofs are recognised as protecting the waterproof membranes of roofs from the effects of temperature variations, ultra violet (UV) radiation and other climatic factors (see Section 8.2). Similar benefits can be gained by using green walls.

During the operational life of a building, management and maintenance aspects of a green roof will be considered, but these will largely depend on the type of system used and how it should look.

On commercial buildings in Europe it is generally accepted that after a number of years green roofs are not maintained, as building service managers take the view that it is not worth the expense. Such roofs then develop into more natural systems. Where such natural vegetation is intentionally planned for and created it can help to keep out species that are less desirable, for example, plants that may be detrimental to roof membranes and the integrity of the building.

In contrast to the design stage, at the operational stage there is often less concern with appearance, especially where green roofs or walls are not overlooked by people.

Construction and development context: Key points

A carefully designed and constructed bespoke roof offers many advantages that can include:

- lower construction costs
- lower maintenance costs
- maximum biodiversity provision to suit local needs
- design of overlooked areas for maximum aesthetic benefits.

Green roofs can provide benefits during construction, as once installed they can protect the water proofing from continuing works.

Critical issues that need to be considered during construction of green roofs and walls include:

- health and safety
- how materials will be transported to the roof
- impact on construction programme
- requirements for temporary protection or support.

Green roofs protect waterproof membranes from environmental damage and prolong their life by a significant amount. Similar benefits can be gained for the building walls by using green walls.

Maintenance is not usually critical for green roofs. Without it they tend to simply develop into more natural systems.

B Green roofs

Holyrood (the Scottish Parliament), Edinburgh (courtesy P Early)

5 INTRODUCTION TO GREEN ROOFS

5.1 Historical perspective

Green roofs of turf construction were a common element found in vernacular styles of buildings in Northern Europe. Even in 1900 over 50 per cent of the inhabitants of Iceland still lived in turf-roofed buildings (International Council on Monuments and Sites, 2005). Examples of these traditional methods of construction can still be found preserved in Northern Scotland, Iceland and other Scandinavian countries.

Figure 5.1

Reconstruction of a traditional crofters house with a turf roof, Rackwick Bay, Hoy, Orkney Isles (courtesy P Early)

These traditional vernacular styles of building gradually came to an end during the 19th century. A major contributing factor was almost certainly the increased availability of cheap, reliable, low maintenance roofing materials that resulted from the industrial revolution. The improved social status inferred by living in a house made from modern materials and built to a modern design may also have contributed to the loss of many vernacular styles and methods of building.

Figure 5.2

Traditional green roof covered cold store, Germany (courtesy P Early)

Renewed interest in green roofs began to develop at the end of the 19th century in Germany where they were used for their fire retarding properties. In many respects these roofs are comparable with modern extensive green roofs (see Section 5.4.3). A number of these roofs still survive, demonstrating the potential durability of green roofing systems (Figure 5.2).

Figure 5.3 *Green roof installed in the 1920s, Berlin, Germany (courtesy Marco Schmidt)*

In the early 20th century, architects such as Le Corbusier, Walter Gropius and Frank Lloyd Wright embraced the concept of green roofs and roof gardens, largely for their amenity value (Figure 5.3). Le Corbusier is considered one of the first systematic "roof greeners". In his five points of new architecture, written in 1923, roof gardens came second.

Frank Lloyd Wright incorporated a green roof into his ground-breaking *Fallingwater* house completed in 1937, which was voted the best all-time work of American architecture by the American Institute of Architects (DiCorcia, 2002).

Two examples of high profile roof gardens constructed in the UK are those on The Lawn Road Flats (Isokon Building), Hampstead, London, constructed between 1933-1934, and on the building still known as *Derry and Toms* in High Street, Kensington, London. The roof gardens of *Derry and Toms*, laid out between 1936–8, still exist as originally conceived.

Less glamorous but more numerous uses of green roofs during the 20th century have been as coverings for municipal buildings, such as car parks (Figure 5.4), small water reservoirs (Figure 5.5) and military buildings including aircraft hangers and bunkers. Some of these, especially those in urban situations, are now designated for their wildlife interest, such as Claremont Square Reservoir in Islington which dates back to 1856.

Figure 5.4 *The extensive green roof on the King Alfred Centre car park on the seafront in Hove, built in 1939 (courtesy P Early)*

Figure 5.5 *Ditchling Road covered reservoir, Brighton (courtesy P Early)*

5.2 Conventional roofs

Roofs are either pitched or flat. A pitched roof is defined as a roof with a slope of greater than 10° (Harrison, 2000), and is usually constructed of ceramic, stone, slate or concrete tiles or metal sheet, supported on a wooden or metal substructure. For the majority of pitched roofs the insulation is usually incorporated below the waterproof membrane.

A flat roof is defined as a roof with a slope of 10° or less (Harrison, 2000). Typically it comprises a deck covered with either a bitumen waterproof layer with a gravel covering, a plastic sheet waterproof membrane, a fluid applied membrane, or an all-metal construction. However, they can be made from a variety of materials including concrete.

Flat roofs are normally categorised as one of the following three types, depending upon the location of the insulation and waterproofing membrane:

Warm Insulation is placed between the exterior waterproof layer of the roof and the roof deck (the deck being the surface that supports the waterproof layer and transfers roof surface loads to structural members). A vapour control layer is placed between insulation and waterproof layer to reduce condensation. No internal ventilation of the roof interior is required.

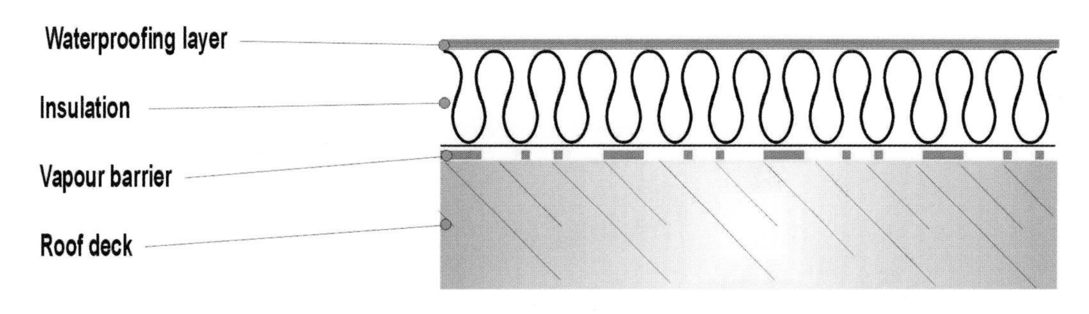

Figure 5.6 *Typical warm flat roof (after Harrison, 2000)*

Inverted warm The insulation is located on the exterior of the roof waterproof layer. The waterproof layer now becomes the vapour control layer preventing condensation between itself and the deck. The thermal insulation protects the waterproof layer from extremes of temperature. The thermal insulation is commonly retained in place by ballast consisting of paving slabs or gravel.

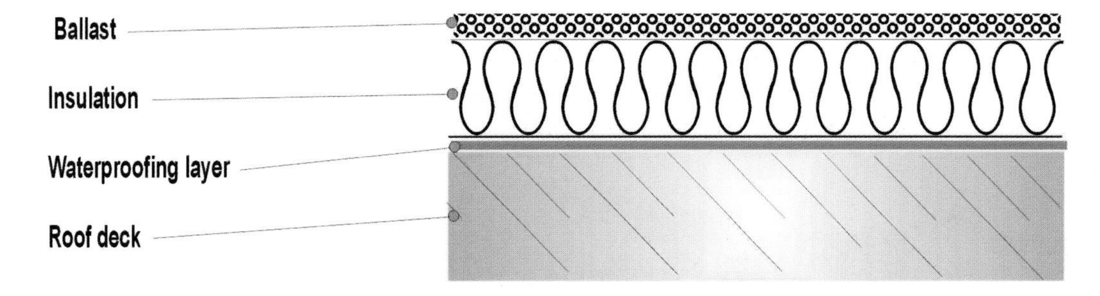

Figure 5.7 *Typical inverted warm flat roof (after Harrison, 2000)*

Cold The insulation is located on the interior side of the deck. The deck is not warmed by the building interior and ventilation is required above the insulating layer to reduce condensation. In the relatively humid climate of the UK the cold deck roof is generally not preferred. In order to protect the waterproofing material, rounded coarse gravel is often used. This reduces temperature fluctuations and the effects of direct UV radiation.

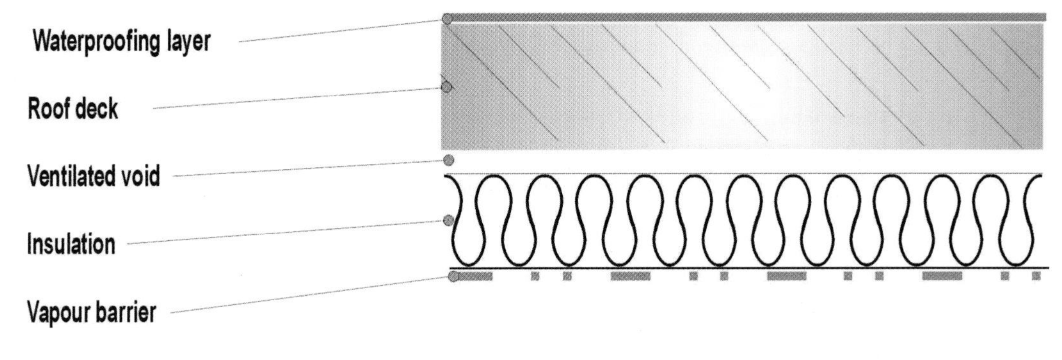

Figure 5.8 *Typical cold flat roof (after Harrison, 2000)*

5.3 The green roof

Conventional roofs, while successfully keeping out the elements, may be regarded as a missed opportunity. With a little more consideration they can be turned into a resource that can bring substantial environmental and amenity benefits. The roof of a recently constructed hospital in London (Figure 5.9a) provides an example of such a missed opportunity. The hospital is located in a city centre site and could have included a green roof within the design, with all the environmental benefits that it would bring, rather than the concrete paving slab ballasted roof that was chosen. The green roof could have been used as a valuable amenity space for patients and staff. Similar comments apply to the housing development in Figure 5.9b.

Figure 5.9 *Conventional inverted roofs (courtesy P Early)*

Contrast these roofs with an example of a biodiverse green roof from the Klinikum 2 building of University Hospital, Basel, Switzerland (Figure 5.10). Here the green roof provides visual interest for those overlooking it, as well as the biodiversity benefit for which it was primarily designed.

Figure 5.10 *The Klinikum green roof (courtesy P Early)*

Cross-sections showing the typical layers in a green roof for the three different categories of roof construction outlined in Section 5.2 are shown in Figure 5.11. Green roofs constructed on pitched or flat roofs generally have a similar build up. However, the stability of the layers on a pitched roof and the water retention characteristics require careful assessment. A restraint system may be required to prevent the substrate from sliding down the roof (see Section 9.5).

When constructing a green roof on an inverted warm roof, where the insulation is above the waterproofing layer, the following features should be incorporated into the design:

- extruded polystyrene insulation should be used (or other material that is impervious to water) to avoid the insulation becoming saturated
- in order to avoid forming a vapour barrier above the insulation the root barrier should always be placed below the insulation. This is because the extruded polystyrene insulation is not impervious to water vapour
- sufficient soil weight needs to be specified to prevent wind uplift or flotation of the insulation.

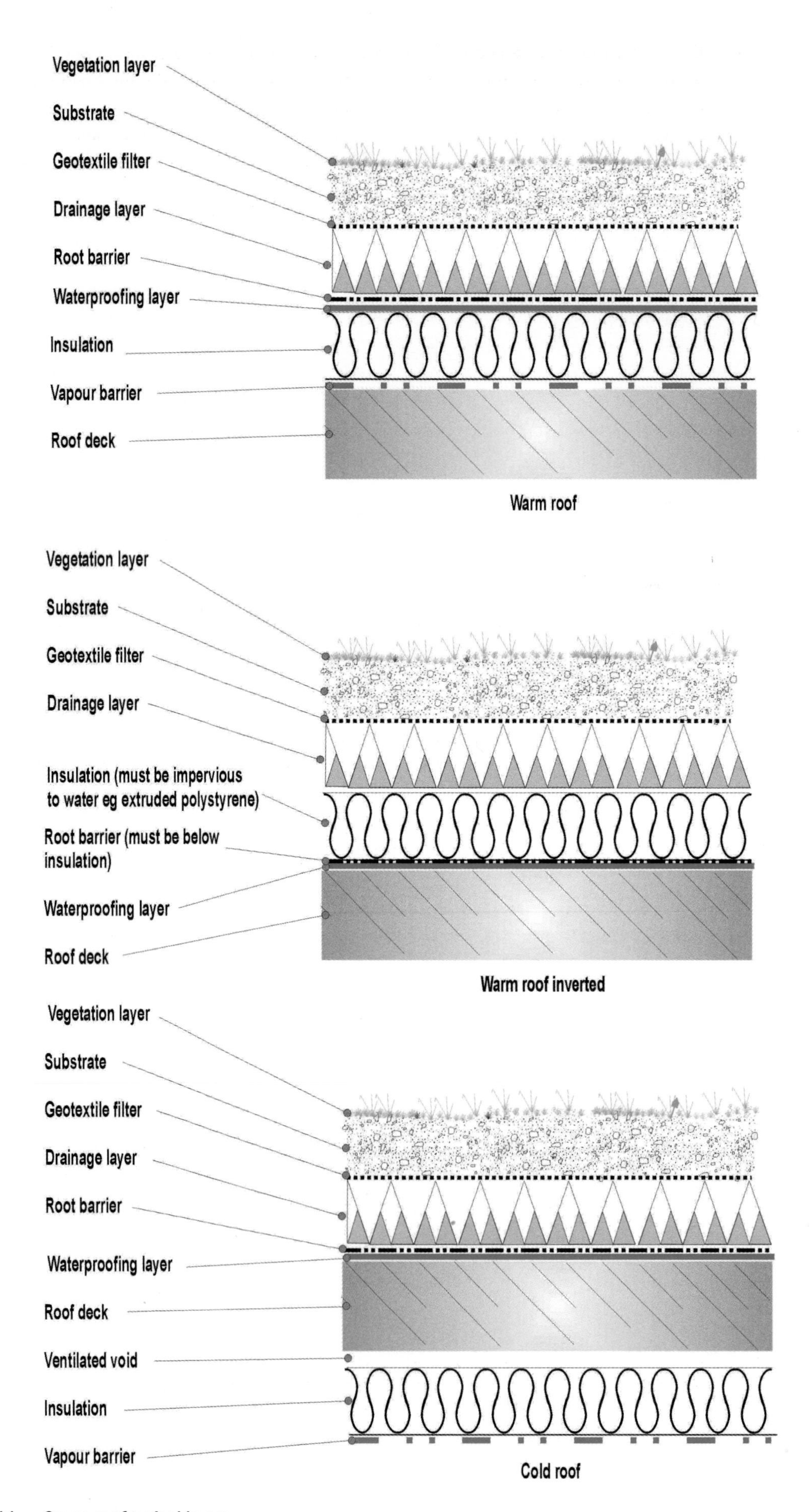

Figure 5.11 *Green roof typical layers*

Until recently the use of green roofs in the UK has largely been restricted to small or landmark developments. This is beginning to change with increasing interest among construction industry professionals in sustainable building design and the contribution that green roofs can make towards it. Typically, modern green roofs are viewed as an integral part of the environmental performance of a building (Dunnett and Kingsbury, 2004).

Green roofs are more common in continental Europe, particularly Germany, Austria and Switzerland, and the UK specialist green roof manufacturers and suppliers tend, with a few exceptions, to represent established German or Swiss companies.

5.4 Types of green roof

The term "green roof" covers roofs, balconies and terraces. It includes roofs that are used by people as public open space and those that are deliberately inaccessible. The majority are flat or of low pitch.

In English language publications it is common to see green roofs categorised as being:

1. *Extensive* – with thin soil, little or no irrigation requirements, low water retention and nutrient poor conditions for plants
2. *Intensive* – with deep soil, irrigation requirements, high water retention and fertile conditions for plants.

However, in recognition of leading German speaking countries in all aspects of green roof design and implementation, this document follows the definitions of the German FLL guidelines (FLL, 2002). These split the types of green roof into three categories based on their intended use, design, and construction type. In addition to the two categories above, the FLL guidelines add:

3. *Simple intensive* – constructed using various substrate depths, thus combining elements of extensive and intensive roofs.

A cross-section showing the typical make up of each type of green roof is shown in Figure 5.12.

A number of other terms currently used to describe green roofs are summarised in Table 5.1.

Table 5.1 ***Alternative terms for green roofs***

Term	Description
Roof gardens	This term is commonly used in the USA and UK and usually refers to green roofs that are intensive or simple intensive and accessible to people.
Eco-roofs	A general term for green roofs – intensive or extensive – first used in Oregon, USA, which has since been adopted by a number of ecologists in the UK (Liptan and Strecker, 2003).
Living roofs	A term coined by Paul Kephart of Rana Creek, USA. It includes roofs that are used by people for recreation, and that may be intensive, extensive or not vegetated at all.
Brown roof/ rubble roof	A term that was first used by biodiversity professionals in the London area to differentiate between the use of generic green roof systems and bespoke systems, in order to provide compensation for the loss of brownfield habitat (Gedge, 2003). The term refers to a roof that has been designed to provide specific benefits for biodiversity.

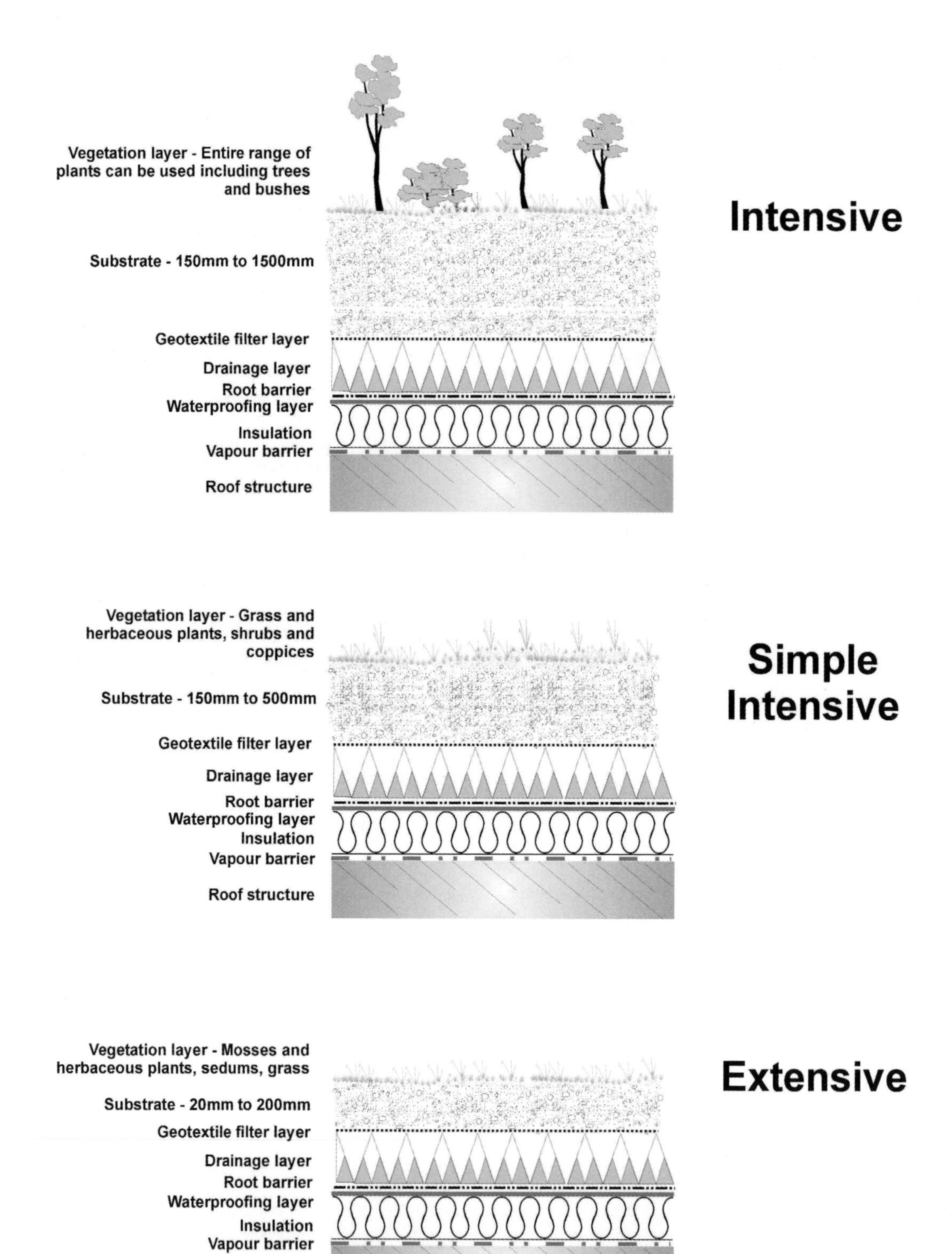

Figure 5.12 *Types of green roof*

5.4.1 Intensive green roofs

With a substrate depth of over 150 mm, the vegetation used for intensive green roofs comprises herbaceous plants, shrubs, grasses and, in some cases, trees. Intensive green roofs are comparable to open spaces at ground level and can allow human access if adequate safety provision has been made (Figure 5.13). As a result of the size of plants that can be used, the depth of the substrate, and the ability of the substrate to hold significant volumes of water, the weight of the intensive green roof system can be considerable. Substantial reinforcement of an existing roof structure or inclusion of extra building structural support may be required. Intensive green roofs require a large amount of maintenance, regular irrigation and applications of fertiliser.

Figure 5.13 *Intensive roof, Jubilee Park, Canary Wharf (courtesy G Kadas)*

5.4.2 Simple intensive green roofs

The vegetation of simple intensive green roofs usually comprises grasses, herbaceous plants and shrubs (Figures 5.14 and 5.15). They can be constructed using varying depths of substrate, thus combining elements of extensive and intensive roofs. Compared to an intensive green roof, the potential for using the roof for amenity purposes is generally limited. The loads imposed by this type of construction are not as great as for an intensive green roof, and the plants used require less irrigation and fertilisation.

Figure 5.14 *Simple intensive green roof (courtesy N Dunnett)*

Figure 5.15 *Simple intensive green roof (courtesy D Gedge)*

5.4.3 Extensive green roofs

Extensive green roofs have a thin growing medium (which can comprise recycled materials), require minimal maintenance, and normally do not require irrigation, although they may require it initially until plants become established. They are usually less costly to install than intensive green roofs and are less costly to maintain as they do not require mowing or any other form of intensive management. Generally they are planted with, or colonised by, mosses, succulents, wild flowers and grasses that are able to survive on the shallow low-nutrient substrates that form their growing medium. Commercial systems in the UK generally use sedums (*sedum spp.)* as the principal plant species in the vegetation layer. Sedums, which are low growing succulents, are favoured as they are drought and wind tolerant, form a dense covering and are attractive to the eye.

There are three main types of extensive green roof system currently available or promoted in the UK:

1 **Sedum mats** – pre-grown blankets of sedum plants on rock wool or similar 2050 mm of growing medium, and rolled out on to the roof membranes. Some suppliers add a wildflower seed mix to the system.

2 **Substrate based roof** – "plugs" of sedum species inserted, or other species hydro-seeded, into 75 mm of growing medium (Figure 5.16).

Figure 5.16 *A plug planted sedum roof after one year of growth (courtesy P Early)*

3 **Green/brown roofs for biodiversity** – extensive green roofs that are designed to meet specific biodiversity targets. These generally require a bespoke designed system using locally characteristic substrates and plants (Figure 5.17).

Figure 5.17 *Construction of a green roof designed for biodiversity, Switzerland (courtesy S Wilson)*

Extensive green roofs are low in maintenance, but many suppliers recommend weeding and fertilising to ensure that the desired plant communities become established. If this is not carried out then natural colonisation may change the nature of the plant communities on the roof. There is a German adage that states *"…one year sedums, two years sedums some grass, three years grass and some sedums, and four years grass"*.

Bespoke green roof systems such as those designed for biodiversity are intended to be self-maintaining systems wherever possible. They are generally the cheapest systems to establish on a roof as vegetation cover tends to consist of wildflowers and grasses, often introduced through natural colonisation. A cross-section of an extensive green roof with varying thicknesses of substrate to provide different areas of habitat is shown in Figure 5.18:

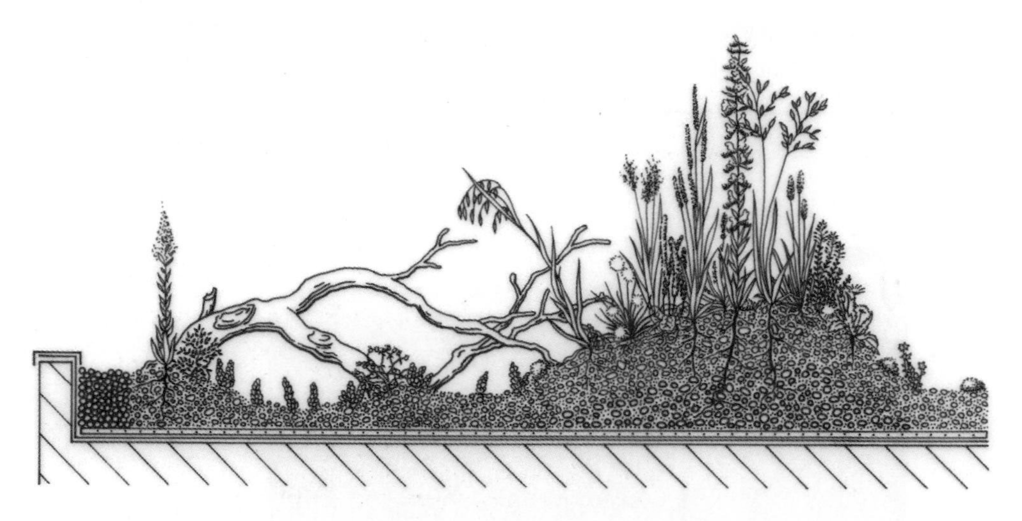

Figure 5.18 *Cross-section of extensive green roof system with varying substrate thickness (courtesy Livingroofs.org)*

5.5 Window boxes, balconies and planters

Window boxes and potted plants are an important element in the overall greening of a building. They provide visual enhancement for occupants and habitat for common species of wildlife in urban areas.

Figure 5.19 *The large irrigated planters of Brunel Street car park, Birmingham provide a valuable habitat and visual enhancement (courtesy P Early)*

There are many variations of design for window boxes, balconies and planters which are not covered within this guidance. However, there are numerous books and websites on gardening that contain information on setting out window boxes and planters (for example Hendy, 1997).

Introduction to green roofs: Key points

- roofs fall into two broad categories – pitched (slope >10°) or flat (slope <10°). Green roofs can be constructed on both types, although substrate restraint systems may be required on sloping roofs
- a flat roof is normally one of the following three types listed below. The type of roof construction has an impact on the design and cost of the green roof

Type of roof	Defining feature	Impacts on green roof design
Warm deck	Insulation is placed between the exterior waterproof layer and the roof deck.	The green roof adds additional load but protects the waterproof layer.
Inverted warm deck	Insulation is located on the exterior of the roof waterproof layer (should be impervious to water). The insulation is typically held in place by ballast.	The green roof can replace the ballast, with the possibility of no extra load. The root barrier should always be placed below the insulation. Sufficient weight of soil is required to hold down the insulation.
Cold deck	The insulation is located on the interior side of the deck.	The green roof adds additional load, but protects the waterproof layer.

- there are three types of green roof based on their use, design, and construction type. These categories determine the selection of plants and vegetation:

Type of green roof	Key features	
Intensive	Substrate depth: Vegetation: Public access: Weight: Maintenance: Cost:	150–1500 mm All types, including shrubs and trees Likely to be a design feature Usually high, with structural support a key design issue in most cases Usually high, with regular irrigation and fertiliser required in most cases High
Simple intensive	Substrate depth: Vegetation: Public access: Weight: Maintenance: Cost:	150–500 mm Grasses, herbaceous plants and shrubs Possible, but may be limited Moderate, with structural support a potential design issue Moderate. May require irrigation and fertiliser, but not on a regular basis Moderate
Extensive	Substrate depth: Vegetation: Public access: Weight: Maintenance: Cost:	20–200 mm Mosses, succulents, wildflowers and grasses No Light, with structural support unlikely to restrict implementation in most cases Very low. Generally only required until plants become established. Low

- window boxes, balconies and potted plants are an important element in the overall greening of a building and can compliment green roofs and walls.

6 BENEFITS OF GREEN ROOFS FOR BIODIVERSITY

6.1 Introduction

Green roofs have considerable potential to provide biodiversity benefits. This has been recognised for some time with, for instance, many of the green roofs constructed in Germany in the early 1970s designed specifically to mitigate for the loss of calcareous grassland habitat in development.

However, as policy drivers have changed, so to has green roof design. As mentioned in Section 2.1, stormwater management has become an increasingly strong driver in Germany for the incorporation of green roofs in the urban environment. This driver led to the design of green roofs that favoured plants that could not only survive in the harsh and exposed environment of the roof, but could also take up and hold a significant amount of water, such as sedums (Keeley, 2005). This approach has led to the development of generic extensive green roof systems that are primarily sedum based, and consequently are of restricted value for biodiversity.

Biodiversity and stormwater management need not, and should not, be opposing objectives. Indeed, the enhancement and creation of wildlife habitat is a key aim of the sustainable drainage approach. As illustrated in Section 2.1, stormwater management performance can be maintained in biodiverse systems (local substrates and plant species) through the use of deeper substrates. Additionally, other plant types such as mosses have been found to be very effective at delaying rainwater runoff (Lundberg, 2005. See Appendix 3).

More recently in Switzerland there has been a move towards biodiverse systems that reflect local nature conservation issues, and that use local seeds and substrates to ensure that the habitats created are relevant to the location (Brenneisen, 2003). This approach is now being explored in the UK and North America.

6.2 Potential

There is a growing realisation that green roofs can help deliver national, regional and local biodiversity action plan targets in both the urban and the rural context (see Section 3.3).

In urban areas there is particular interest in the use of extensive green roofs as mitigation for the loss of brownfield habitat. Brownfield land often provides extremely valuable wildlife habitat. Extensive green roofs tend to be similar in character to brownfield land, with both having substrate that is generally well-drained and nutrient poor (Gedge and Kadas, 2004).

A report for English Nature (Grant *et al*, 2003) lists the contributions that green roofs can make to the conservation and enhancement of biodiversity. They include:

- helping to remedy areas of deficiency, ie providing new habitat in areas which are currently lacking in wildlife habitat
- creating new links in an intermittent network of habitats, thereby facilitating movement and dispersal of wildlife
- providing additional habitat for rare, protected or otherwise important species.

A green roof system is an attempt to artificially create ground level habitat on a roof, using plants and a growing medium, and with groundwater being provided by moisture mats and irrigation boards. It is possible to replicate the key features of a variety of habitats, such as sand dune, or chalk grassland on a roof. In most cases the primary determinant of vegetation/habitat type will be the amount of water that can be held within a system. Ephemeral, ruderal and grassland communities will typically develop on extensive green roof systems, and deeper rooted species such as trees and shrubs on more intensive systems (Boscoe, 2003).

There is a common misconception that green roofs will follow natural plant succession, with grassland turning to scrub and finally to woodland. This is not the case. Extensive green roofs tend to develop into natural self-sustaining grassland communities as the limitations of the system will not allow for further plant succession. For intensive green roof systems it is human intervention ie the intentional incorporation of plants and regular maintenance, that ensures that the system performs as it was designed to.

6.3 Limitations

All systems, regardless of the depth of substrate and the planting regime, will provide some benefit for wildlife. However, if a green roof is required to meet a specific biodiversity objective then there is a need for specialist ecological input to ensure that the roof is successful. In most cases the use of a generic green roof system will not be suitable and an ecologist can advise on the development of a bespoke system (Gedge and Kadas, 2005).

Green roofs will not perform in the same way as habitats at ground level, but the use of similar substrates at similar depths with local and appropriate seed mixes should enable the key features of the ground level habitat to be created. Caution should be exercised, as certain elements within ground level habitat may not be appropriate in a roof situation. For example, vigorous plants such as bramble *Rubus fruticosus* and butterfly bush *Buddleja davidii* can have a detrimental effect on roofs (spread quickly and take over the whole roof), so would not be appropriate for inclusion, even though they may be an important element at ground level.

The English Nature report (Grant *et al*, 2003) identifies some limitations of green roofs as ground level habitat replacement. They include:

- the area of habitat is likely to be smaller
- the components required to create the habitat at roof level may be too heavy for the proposed building
- it may not be possible to replicate the habitat quickly enough after demolition to ensure conservation of important species
- it may result in the habitat being isolated at roof level rather than contiguous with other habitat at ground level.

Visual appearance may also be a limiting factor. For example, a school in Hampshire decided against a generic system, opting instead to install the growing medium themselves. Several years later, although the roof had *"a positive abundance of insects and could win an award for biodiversity..."* school managers were concerned with the roofs appearance. As this example illustrates, the design of a successful green roof will often require consideration of the interests of different stakeholders. However, solutions can be found. For example, it may be that areas of the roof that are overlooked use an aesthetically pleasing system, while areas that are out of sight are designed to maximise biodiversity.

6.4 Benefits for biodiversity

There has been considerable research on green roof plant ecology to establish which plants perform best in various types and depths of substrates (Dunnett and Kingsbury, 2004). This work has largely been driven by aesthetics and the need to assess the ability of plants to retain water. Only relatively recently has research been undertaken on the broader benefits of biodiversity. A detailed overview of current research into the benefits of green roofs for flora and fauna is provided in Appendix 2. The key points are summarised in Sections 6.4.1 to 6.4.4.

6.4.1 Mosses

There is a great deal of potential for mosses to form an element of the green roof flora, and more specifically there is potential to design nutrient poor systems to encourage scarce and uncommon species. Limited research has been undertaken in the UK to date, but two nationally scarce species, *Aloina ambigua* and *Thuidium abietinum spp. abietinum* have been found on green roofs in London. A number of other species have been unexpectedly discovered including *Amblystegium serpens*, *Camplyopus introflexus* and *Camplyopus pyriformis* (Moller, 2005).

6.4.2 Other plants

The variety of plant species suited to the green roof environment varies significantly with green roof type. The nutrient rich and often relatively sheltered conditions of accessible intensive green roofs allow a wide variety of plant species, similar to those found in gardens and parks, to flourish. At the other end of the spectrum, the nutrient poor, free draining and exposed environment of a high level extensive green roof limits the range of suitable species. However, an increasing body of research on the continent and more recently in the UK is highlighting an increasing diversity of native and non-native plant species suited to these harsh conditions.

In Germany, the focus of green roof research has been primarily on plant species associated with dry meadow communities and alpine habitats; including low growing grasses such as *Festuca spp.* and species of the Dianthus family. A number of other interesting species have been researched for their viability as green roof plants including thymes *Thymus spp.*, *Alisons Alyssum spp.*, onion family *Allium spp.*, bell flowers *Campanula spp.* and cinquefoils *Potentilla spp.* (Kolb and Schwarz, 1999). An excellent example of the diversity of plant life that can be achieved on green roofs is the Moos Water Filtration Plant in Zurich, Switzerland (see Case study 3) which has been designated a National Park on the basis of the plant diversity (which included many rare species the most notable being green-winged orchid *Orchis morio*).

In the UK, studies such as that undertaken at the Eden Project in Cornwall have noted a number of species that can be seeded onto green roofs with good results, including horseshoe *vetch Hippocrepis comosa* and kidney vetch *Anthyllis vulneraria*. These are both important food plants for a number of butterflies (Jenrick, 2005). The need to balance the needs of biodiversity and aesthetics in green roof plantings, through the use of native and non-native species, has also been considered in work undertaken at Sheffield University (Dunnett, 2006).

6.4.3 Invertebrates

Many brownfield sites provide habitat for a wide range of rare invertebrates. For example, the shallow gravel workings and derelict land in the East Thames Corridor have been found to support a remarkable concentration of rare invertebrates (Harvey, 2001). UK biodiversity action plan species such as the brown banded bumble bee *Bombus humilis* and shrill carder bee *Bombus sylvarum*, are both found on such sites and on many occasions are restricted to these habitats. Consequently, the redevelopment of brownfield sites can be detrimental to local, regional and national biodiversity interests.

Recently there has been a significant amount of research into the benefits of green roofs for invertebrates associated with brownfield land, including species of bee, wasp, spider, beetle etc, and the role green roofs can play in mitigating for the loss of brownfield habitat. Studies in Switzerland and, latterly, the UK have shown that green roofs of all types can provide habitat for invertebrate species. However, a number of studies have shown that where the green roof is to be used as mitigation for rare brownfield invertebrate communities, simple proprietary sedum based systems will not meet biodiversity objectives (Gedge and Kadas, 2005). Diversity will be encouraged by designing more naturalistic bespoke systems with specific features incorporated, such as boulders, logs and bare areas of substrate (Brenneisen, 2001).

Research has found that naturalistic dry grassland roofs are the most productive for bees (including the brown banded bumble bee) and associated species as they provide rich foraging habitat throughout the year. Although sedums provide a good source of nectar for wild bees, the flowering period is limited and this reduces their value. Similar findings have been made in respect of other invertebrates and this reinforces the need to carefully design roofs to achieve specific biodiversity targets.

Figure 6.1 *Cornflower and bumble bee (courtesy S Brenneisen)*

Figure 6.2 *Basel green roof designed for rare invertebrates, (a) during construction and (b) one year after completion (courtesy D Gedge)*

The following design principles, which have been developed from Swiss research, set out the key factors to consider when seeking to attract a rich diversity of invertebrates to green roofs:

- use varied and appropriate substrate materials
- use varied substrate depths

- provide varied vegetation types using local seed mixes
- use boulders and dry wood logs to provide habitat on the green roof.

The implementation of these principles is illustrated in Figure 6.2. In the Canton of Basel it is now a legal requirement that all green roofs are designed for rare invertebrates in-line with the principles outlined above.

6.4.4 Birds

The English Nature Research Report 498 *Green Roofs: their existing status and potential for conserving biodiversity in urban areas* (Grant *et al*, 2003) highlights that there is great potential for green roofs to provide benefits for nine bird species listed in the National, London and Birmingham biodiversity action plans, and the biodiversity audits for London and East Anglia. These are kestrel *Falco tinnunculus*, swallow *Hirundo rustica*, house martin *Delichon urbica*, pied wagtail *Motacilla alba*, black redstart *Phoenicurus ochruros*, song thrush *Turdus philomelos*, house sparrow *Passer domesticus*, goldfinch *Carduelis carduelis* and greenfinch *Carduelis chloris*. Many other species have been found on green roofs. A short study of green roofs in Sussex in 2004, noted ringed plover *Charadrius hiaticula*, little ringed plover, *Charadrius dubius*, skylark *Alauda arvensis*, songthrush *Turdus philomelos*, starling *Sturnus vulgaris* and linnet *Carduelis cannabina* (Burgess, 2004).

Research is currently being undertaken on how green roofs can be improved to encourage different species. As with invertebrates, generic roof systems in urban situations are likely to provide habitat for more common species of bird, whereas roofs specifically designed to mimic habitats within the urban fabric, such as brownfield sites, are likely to be more successful for species such as black redstart *Phoenicurus ochruros*.

Factors to take into account when considering green roofs as mitigation for the loss, or replication of ground level habitat include:

- size of roof area, which is likely to affect the attractiveness for invertebrate species and consequently the composition of bird species
- the relationship of the building to local terrestrial habitats that will act as a source for colonisation and may act as wider habitat for the species
- the inclusion of habitat mosaics (two or more habitat types) and specific elements (logs, boulders etc) that benefit key species.

Figure 6.3 *Spontaneous green roof on which lapwings breed (courtesy D Gedge)*

Case study 3 Moos Filtration Plant, Zurich, Switzerland

Green-winged orchid, Moos Filtration Plant (courtesy S Wilson)

Moos Filtration Plant (courtesy G Grant

Type of development	Filtration plant
Reason for green roof	Built in 1913 the reservoir roofs were originally exposed concrete decks with waterproofing. The water beneath became too hot in the summer so a green roof was installed in later years to insulate the reservoir and cool the water beneath.
Type of green roof	Naturally colonised extensive green roof
Build up	80 mm concrete deck with mastic asphalt waterproofing 150–200 mm local meadow soils laid on 50 mm sand.
Planting	The soils were not seeded but have developed a rich central Swiss wet meadow community through natural colonisation. The meadow reflects the richness of local agricultural meadows at the turn of the twentieth century.
Size	30 000 m^2
Comments	The meadow has 175 species of higher plant many of which are rare and endangered at both a local and national level. For example, there are nine species of orchids, including 6000 green-winged orchids *Orchis morio*.

Case study 4 Jacob Burckhardt Haus Basel, Switzerland

Courtesy Livingroofs.org

Type of development	Commercial offices
Reason for green roof	To fulfil local and federal policy regarding green roofs. They had to be designed to fulfil local legislation regarding the provision of habitat for biodiversity.
Type of green roof	Extensive biodiverse system
Build up	✧ sandy local gravels, Ricoter green roof soil ✧ depth varied between 80 and 150 mm.
Planting	Basel seed mix
Size	6000 m^2
Architect	Zwimpfer Partners and Krarup Furer Architects
Comments	The green roof build up provides a mosaic of habitats for bird and invertebrate species, using a mix of commercial green roof soils planted with sedums, and areas of gravel and sand seeded with a local seed mix.

Case study 5 Komodo Dragon House, London Zoo, UK

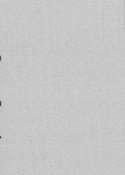

Type of development	Accommodation for the first pair of Komodo Dragons ever to be housed at London Zoo
Reason for green roof	Planning requirement as the development is overlooked by Regents Park, and as part of the Zoo's sustainability policy.
Type of green roof	Extensive biodiverse green roof system
Build up	⟡ 18 mm plywood deck ⟡ loose laid polyethylene vapour control layer ⟡ CFC and HCFC extruded polystyrene thermal insulation board. Single ply membrane loose laid with all overlaps hot air welded (FLL approved for use without an additional root barrier) ⟡ 20 mm recycled polyethylene drainage and protection board ⟡ 65–150 mm of growing medium consisting of recycled crushed brick and graded earth from site, in a mix of either 80 per cent brick to 20 per cent earth of 80 per cent earth to 20 per cent brick ⟡ areas of shingle and sand.
Planting	Calcareous seed mix and plug plants used to create the vegetation.
Size	300 m^2
Client	Zoological Society of London
Architect	Kozdon Wharmby
Designer	The Green Roof Consultancy
Main contractor	ITC Concepts Ltd
Roofing contractor	Miller Roofing Ltd
Comments	The design is based on principles developed in Switzerland for biodiversity and adapted for London by Livingroofs.org. These principles include: ⟡ use varied and appropriate substrate materials ⟡ use varied substrate depths ⟡ provide varied vegetation types using local seed mixes ⟡ use boulders and dry wood logs to provide habitat on the green roof.
Completion date	February 2006

Case study 6 1 Churchill Place, Canary Wharf, London, UK

Courtesy Livingroofs.org

Type of development	Commercial tower
Reason for green roof	*"Barclays takes its environmental responsibilities very seriously and this was an ideal opportunity to do something different and to innovate. One Churchill Place was built on reclaimed land, ensuring no loss of greenfield space in the area. Adding the living-roof provides one of our most endangered neighbours (black redstart) with additional habitat and contributes positively to biodiversity and the local community. The reaction of our staff to the new addition has been amazing".* (Nita Patel, Barclays Environmental Manager)
Type of green roof	Extensive biodiverse system, retro fitted onto paving
Build up	✧ locally sourced recycled crushed brick and concrete substrate (from Charlton, South London) with pine bark, shingle and small area of sedum mat ✧ erosion mat required to prevent wind erosion as vegetation establishes.
Planting	Sedum mat and calcareous grassland and special cornflower seed mix
Size	400 m^2
Client	Barclays Bank plc
Architect	HOK (not involved in roof design)
Roofing contractor	TCL GRANBY and COVERITE
Comments	This green roof has been designed to Swiss principles. There are three mosaic habitats: 1 Sedum mat to give instant green cover which will eventually turn to grassland. 2 Shingle areas to provide bare areas for xeric invertebrates. 3 Calcareous grassland mix to provide structured vegetation for invertebrates. The roof is the highest in the UK and Europe, and possibly the highest in the world, designed specifically for biodiversity (35 storeys high).
Completion date	June 2005

Case study 7 Zurich Main Railway Station, Switzerland

View of roof (courtesy Livingroofs.org)

Close up showing gabion pillars to provide connection to the ground (courtesy S Wilson)

Structure and substrate depth (courtesy G Grant)

Type of development	Sihlpost Platforms, Zurich Main Railway Station
Reason for green roof	An extension to include four additional platforms at the Zurich main station required a green roof for both stormwater management (including ground level SUDS) and nature conservation (sensitive area with endangered invertebrates and reptiles). There was also a requirement to provide access to the roof for reptiles and less mobile insects through the use of specially designed pillars.
Type of green roof	Extensive
Build up	• waterproofing • 25 mm drainage layer and filter sheet • sandy – loamy gravel, gravel mixed with organic materials • roof garden soil • gravels taken from the site as being constructed • 80 mm depth with mounds up to 300 mm above pillars and crossbeams.
Size	9500 m^2
Comments	The green roof is intended to mimic the habitat at ground level prior to construction. This involved replicating the dry gravel beds associated with Swiss rivers with a specific focus on habitat creation for common wall lizards *Podarcis muralis* and rare invertebrates associated with dry gravel river beds. House sparrows are regularly observed using the roof. The design of the roof demonstrates the potential to design for deeper mounds (in this case 300 mm) above supporting beams and pillars.

Benefits of green roofs for biodiversity: Key points

- green roofs can help deliver national, regional and local biodiversity action plan targets in both the urban and the rural context
- generic extensive green roof systems that are primarily sedum based provide some value for biodiversity. However, where specific species or habitat are to be met, bespoke systems will usually be required
- in urban areas extensive green roofs can be used as mitigation for the loss of brownfield habitat
- the potential biodiversity benefits of green roofs include:
  - providing new habitat in areas which are currently lacking in wildlife habitat
  - creating new links in an intermittent network of habitats
  - providing additional habitat for rare, protected or otherwise important species
- the amount of water that can be held within the green roof construction will largely dictate the type of vegetation it supports. Ephemeral, ruderal and grassland communities will typically develop on extensive green roof systems, and deeper rooted species such as trees and shrubs on intensive systems
- extensive green roofs tend to develop into natural self-sustaining grassland communities as the limitations of the system will not allow for further plant succession
- if a green roof is required to meet a specific biodiversity requirement, it is important to involve a specialist ecological consultant who can advise on habitat creation
- green roofs can replicate many features of ground level habitat. However, certain plant species found in ground level habitat (eg vigorous plants such as bramble *Rubus fruticosus*) may not be appropriate in a roof situation because they may damage the roof structure
- design will be a balancing act to meet the requirements of different stakeholders
- green roofs can provide biodiversity benefits for a wide range of plant, invertebrate and bird species if careful consideration is given at the design stage
- when designing green roofs as mitigation for habitat loss at ground level, the following key factors should be considered:
  - size of roof area, which will affect the composition of plant, invertebrate and consequently bird species
  - the relationship of the building to local terrestrial habitats as part of habitat networks
  - the inclusion of habitat mosaics (ie two or more habitat types) and specific elements (eg logs, boulders, bare areas of gravel) that benefit key species.

7 BENEFITS OF GREEN ROOFS FOR SUSTAINABLE DRAINAGE

7.1 Introduction

In many parts of the world it is recognised that green roofs can provide significant environmental advantage through surface water management. Surface water drainage systems that follow the principles of sustainable development are collectively referred to in the UK as sustainable drainage systems (SUDS). These systems are designed both to manage the adverse environmental consequences resulting from urban runoff (quantity and quality issues – Section 2.3) and to contribute, wherever possible, to environmental enhancement.

SUDS objectives are to:

- replicate natural drainage as closely as possible
- control the quantity and quality of the runoff from development sites
- maximise amenity and biodiversity opportunities.

A fundamental concept of SUDS is the use of source control, ie the control of runoff at or very near its source. Green roofs can contribute to source control objectives and so they are ideal components of sustainable drainage systems.

Historically the main concern of SUDS has been to reduce the peak rate of runoff from sites. However, the latest guidance on managing runoff in SUDS (CIRIA, 2007) emphasises that reducing total volumes of runoff is as important as controlling the peak rates of runoff during individual storms in order to replicate natural catchments and minimise adverse impact on watercourses.

Around 30 to 40 per cent of rainfall events are sufficiently small that there is no measurable runoff taking place from greenfield areas, as it all infiltrates into the soil or evaporates. In contrast, virtually every rainfall event generates some runoff from developed land, resulting in streams and rivers that are prone to rapid changes in water level. In addition, whereas for greenfield areas pollution in runoff from small events is subject to natural filtration processes, runoff from developed land can flush surface pollutants directly into the receiving waters. Where possible the natural greenfield behaviour should be replicated. Ideally, any SUDS system should be designed to prevent runoff from rainfall events of up to 5 mm (this is termed interception storage). Green roofs can meet all these objectives.

An additional benefit is that, by using green roofs, the required volume of surface or underground attenuation storage can potentially be reduced, depending on the design criteria for the site (CIRIA, 2007). This can be particularly important in dense urban developments where space for surface level SUDS components, such as ponds, may be limited. It is also an important consideration when reviewing the cost of a green roof, as there will be a reduction in the requirement for below ground drainage, in the number of downpipes, and in the overall complexity of the pipe network (see Section 10.3).

In countries such as Germany, green roofs are seen as an important tool in mitigating the adverse effects of development on rainfall runoff and for managing urban flood risk.

Research in the UK (Kellagher and Lauchlan, 2005, CIRIA, 2007) indicates that green roofs are effective in providing both attenuation and volume reduction in runoff for small events, but suggests that these advantages are reduced (but not completely lost) for larger events. Green roofs reduce the annual volume of runoff by between 50 and 85 per cent depending on their construction. A green roof will still slow down the rate of runoff even when completely saturated. Providing the performance characteristics of the green roofs are allowed for, there is no reason why green roofs cannot provide a valuable contribution to a SUDS scheme. The performance characteristics depend on the depth and type of substrate that is used (a deeper substrate can hold more water reducing runoff for larger rainfall events). There is, however, a balance to be achieved between increasing the depth of substrate for stormwater management and the effect this will have on other aspects such as the need for increased structural support, biodiversity value and irrigation requirements.

7.2 Stormwater management

When rain hits a green roof it will first be held on plants and absorbed by the substrate (and possibly the drainage layer) in the same manner as a greenfield site. For most small events the rainfall is eventually removed by evapotranspiration. Only when the substrate exceeds its field capacity will water percolate through to the underlying drainage layer in significant volumes.

The green roof influences the runoff hydrograph in two ways:

1. Interception and retention of rainfall from the early part of a storm.
2. Limiting the maximum release rate of runoff in larger storms.

The processes involved in the operation of a green roof are (Tarr, 2002):

- retention of rainwater in substrate, drainage layers and on plants
- uptake of water and release by plants as vapour (evapotranspiration). A case study of measured evapotranspiration rates is provided in Appendix 5 (Case study A5.1)
- uptake of water and biochemical incorporation by plants (photosynthesis)
- evaporation from substrate and foliage.

There is a wealth of published information that demonstrates the performance of green roofs in attenuating stormwater runoff by reducing peak flow rates and volumes (Appendix 3). The performance of a roof depends on the type and depth of construction and particularly the substrate. It also depends on rainfall patterns and season, although this is no different to other SUDS components such as permeable pavements, or indeed greenfield catchments. A typical runoff response of a green roof to rainfall is shown in Figure 7.1.

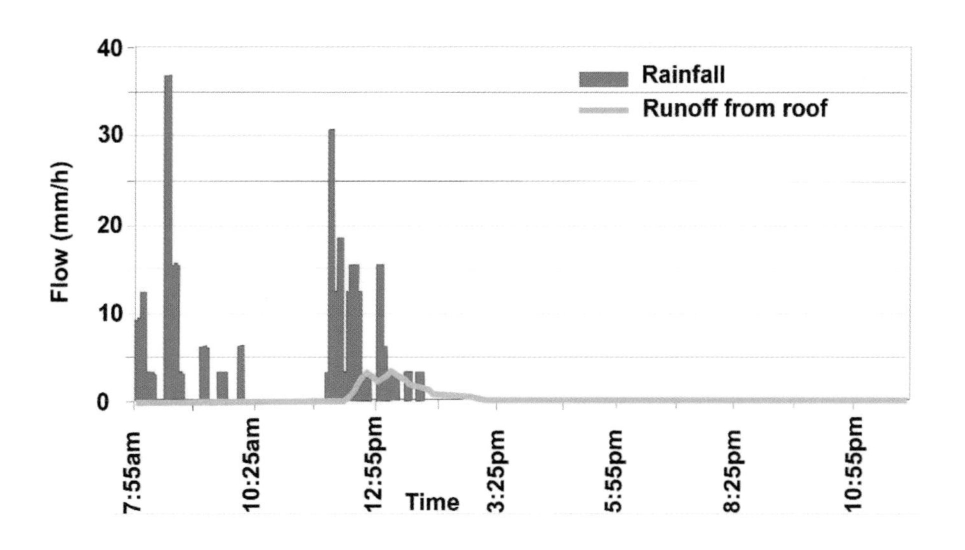

Figure 7.1 *Runoff from green roof (Moran et al, 2005)*

The data in Appendix 3 generally demonstrates that green roofs:

- will intercept the first 5 mm and more of rainfall (provide interception storage)
- are very effective at reducing the volume and rate of runoff from small rainfall events

In the USA a study (Miller, 2006a) analysed the long-term performance of two green roof systems (250 mm and 350 mm thick on a level roof) using simulated rainfall and potential evapotranspiration data from a nearby weather station. The data from this study is summarised in Table 7.1.

Table 7.1 *Performance of green roof 1990 to 1991 (Miller, 2006a)*

Date	Runoff: Rainfall ratio	
	250 mm thick roof	350 mm thick roof
December to February	30 %	16 %
March to May	11 %	7 %
June to August	10 %	4 %
September to November	5 %	0 %
Total annual	**14 %**	**7 %**

Note: Annual rainfall in 1990 was 863 mm and in 1991 was 737 mm.

The data in Table 7.1 shows a significant reduction in runoff volume throughout the year, although the performance is specific to the time of year. Two design storms were then analysed:

1. 25 mm over one hour with a peak rate of 56 mm/h over 10 minutes.
2. 132 mm of rainfall over 24 hours.

No measurable runoff was recorded for the 25 mm event. For the 24 hour event, runoff volume ratios of 58 per cent for the 250 mm thick construction and 38 per cent for the 350 mm thick construction were achieved. The conclusion was that runoff from these green roofs would behave in a similar manner to that from open green space for rainfall up to these levels. The volume of rainfall typically used in SUDS design in the UK is much lower than these values and varies between 51 mm and 82 mm for a 100 year return period, six hour duration event. This study suggests that green roofs can be used to manage long return period events in the UK.

Guidance on the use of SUDS in high density developments (Kellagher and Lauchlan, 2005) suggests that any interception storage provided (in this case by the green roof) reduces the attenuation storage requirement. The runoff characteristics of a green roof should be carefully considered for a range of events and conditions in order to integrate it into the SUDS design, taking into account the type of roof construction used.

Case study 8 shows an example of how green roofs have been used in the UK as part of a SUDS scheme and Case study 9 demonstrates the use of a green roof for stormwater management in Germany.

Case study 8 Norfolk Community Primary School, Sheffield, UK

Views of roof (courtesy (left) C Basilio, (right) Sheffield City Council)

Type of development	Norfolk Community Primary School, Sheffield
Reason for green roof	The green roof was installed to deal with a number of issues including reducing surface water runoff. The main justification for the roof was to solve direct problems of intrusive noise from rain and hail and issues of vandalism on metal deck roofs.
Build up	◇ metal deck ◇ 40 mm vegetation support blanket overlain with 30 mm sedum mats.
Planting	Sedum mats
Size	1684 m²
Comments	Due to sewage and stormwater overflow problems in the local catchment, one design requirement for the new school was to minimise the site's rainwater runoff as part of an holistic water management strategy. Green roofs were chosen for their water holding capacity as an innovative form of sustainable drainage design to relieve pressure on the overloaded drainage system. Excess water runoff from the roof was harvested and utilised to supply the school's toilets. Although only a blanket based roof supporting a thin layer of sedums was installed, the roof serves various purposes, reducing intrusive noise from rain and hail which has been a problem from some of the lightweight long-span metal roofs, improving thermal insulation, providing evaporative cooling, improving rainwater management from the site and creating a habitat for insects and other wildlife (bees were particularly evident in the first season) In the hot summer of 2006 the school remained comfortable and seems to have suffered less from the effects of hot temperatures than other schools in the city. The following simple decisions about the building and its form/environment have played a key part in its success: ◇ the roof has only a 10° pitch (a financial decision) which is the steepest that can be achieved without a water retention/drainage layer ◇ most of the roof slope faces north west and so avoids the worst of the sun ◇ the roof is at several different levels that always offer some shade to wildlife/plants ◇ the only section of the roof visible from the ground is over the main entrance which faces west and is shaded from the worst of the sun, providing the best chance of success. When looking up a 10° slope the perspective always makes it look well vegetated even if there is the odd thin patch.

Case study 9 Potsdamer Platz green roof rainwater management, Berlin, Germany

Extensive green roofs of Potsdamer Platz (courtesy Doehr)

Type of development	Retail (supermarket) Potsdamer Platz, Berlin, Germany
Reason for green roof	Planning constraint for stormwater management so that only 1 per cent of annualised rainwater runoff is allowed from the site.
Type of green roof	Mixture of extensive and intensive
Build up	✧ the extensive green roofs are constructed from low nutrient substrates so as to ensure that the runoff does not compromise other elements of the stormwater system (ie avoid algal growth in the on-site buffer pond) ✧ substrate depths across all the green roofs range between 100–600 mm.
Size	16000 m²
Client	Daimler Chrysler/Debis Immobilienmanagement GmbH
Architects	Renzo Piano & Christoph Kolbecker, Richard Rogers, Hans Kollhoff, Lauber & Woehr, Arata Isozaki, Rafael Moneo.
Green roof landscape architect	Krueger & Moehrle Lanscape Architects (project architect: Daniel Roehr)
Stormwater drainage designer	Marco Schmidt, TU-Berlin
Roofing contractor	Firma Fichter, Firma Leonhards
Comments	The high-profile development of Potsdamer Platz, Berlin was constrained by city planners so that only 1 per cent of annualised rainwater runoff is allowed from the site. This very challenging demand is met by the developments' unique stormwater management and recycling system, which uses green roofs as an integral element of a complex drainage system that includes a large on-site buffer pond and underground storage tanks. Rainwater held within the storage tanks is used for toilet flushing and irrigation of intensive green roofs and green spaces. In all there are 16 000 m² of green roofs, with a mixture of intensive and extensive roofs, within the total 48 000 m² developed area The extensive green roofs are of a specifically low nutrient design, as the green roof runoff provides the water for the buffer lake. This lake is also used as an attractive amenity feature and so must remain clear of algal growth etc that would be encouraged by the over provision of nutrients. The green roofs retain between 60 and 70 per cent of the rainwater hitting their surface, which is then subject to evapotranspiration and hence provides cooling and generally improves the local microclimate. The reuse of on-site stored rainwater water saves approximately 20 000 m³ per year of potable water.
Completion date	1999

7.3 Pollution removal from stormwater runoff

Rainfall runoff from roofs can be polluted (eg from bird droppings or atmospheric pollution) and an important aspect of SUDS is removal of this pollution. Green roofs retain and bind contaminants that are introduced to the surface either as dust or suspended/dissolved in rainwater. Johnston and Newton (2004) stated that 95 per cent of heavy metals are removed from runoff by green roofs and nitrogen levels can be reduced. Auckland Regional Council (2003) advises that green roofs are accepted as removing 75 per cent of total suspended solids (TSS). However, pollutants can leach out of green roof substrate if it is not correctly specified (Koehler and Schmidt, 2003). Careful attention should be paid to the materials to be used in green roof construction, especially when using those that have been reclaimed.

The Pennsylvania Department of Environmental Protection (2004) recommend that, if water quality improvements are a design requirement for a green roof, an engineered substrate with 100 per cent mineral content should be used. This minimises the risk of pollutants leaching out of the substrate. It goes on to recommend that fertiliser should only be used during establishment of vegetation and for as short a period as possible; again this will reduce the risk of the green roof causing rather than preventing pollution. It also states that it takes five or more years for a green roof to reach its maximum pollutant removal efficiency.

Lundberg (2005) reports on the monitoring of green roofs in Sweden where green roof plots were found to remove nitrogen from runoff, but increased the concentrations of phosphorous and potassium. There was little effect on heavy metal concentrations in the runoff.

Other studies have found that pollution removal is variable (see Appendix 4). The most important factors that affect performance are:

- nature of substrate and organic matter content
- type of planting and length of time established
- nature of maintenance (eg application of fertiliser).

7.4 Sustainable water management

With growing concerns about climate change and the impacts this has both on the supply and demand for water, appropriately designed green roofs can contribute to sustainable water management through rainwater harvesting or greywater recycling.

It is likely that water from sustainable water management systems will be used for non-potable (or none wholesome) uses such as irrigation and toilet flushing. However, in some rare occasions these systems can augment drinking water provision with appropriate water treatment systems and testing.

The design and use of green roofs as part of a sustainable water management system should consider the end use of the harvested or reclaimed water (whether for toilet flushing or irrigation etc) and any water quality requirements. The materials used in systems (eg substrate and pipe work) or any fertiliser added may have an impact on water quality. Further information can be found in CIRIA C539 *Rainwater and greywater use in buildings: Best practice* (Leggett *et al*, 2001).

In Berlin a vertical reed bed system was installed on the roof of a residential block to reclaim greywater. Closer to home, this approach has been implemented in a few experimental systems in London where a reed bed system to filter greywater has been designed for installation on building roofs to provide reclaimed water for toilet flushing and irrigation (Water Works UK, 2007).

Benefits of green roofs for sustainable drainage: Key points

- green roofs are ideal components of sustainable drainage systems, contributing to the following SUDS objectives:
  - to replicate natural drainage as closely as possible
  - to control the quantity and quality of the runoff from development sites at or very near its source (source control)
  - to maximise amenity and biodiversity opportunities
- green roofs can:
  - reduce the average annual volume of runoff by between 50 and 85 per cent and prevent runoff for at least the first 5 mm of rainfall depending on the type of construction, ie they provide interception storage
  - attenuate runoff to reduce peak flow rates. This effect is reduced (but not totally lost) for larger or prolonged rainfall events
- by using green roofs, the volume of surface or underground attenuation storage can potentially be reduced, depending on the design criteria for the site
- green roof performance characteristics will depend on the depth and type of substrate that is used and the type of vegetation
- green roofs retain and bind contaminants that are introduced to the surface either as dust or suspended/dissolved in rainwater and reduce pollution of rivers
- green roofs have been shown to remove 95 per cent of heavy metals from runoff in some cases and to reduce nitrogen levels (Johnston & Newton, 2004)
- careful attention should be paid to the materials to be used in green roof construction, especially when using those that have been reclaimed, in order to prevent pollutants leaching out into the rainfall runoff. Where water quality improvements are a design requirement, an engineered substrate with 100 per cent mineral content should be used. Fertiliser should only be used during the establishment of vegetation and for as short a time as possible
- it can take five or more years for a green roof to reach its maximum pollutant removal efficiency.

8 BENEFITS OF GREEN ROOFS FOR CLIMATE CHANGE MITIGATION AND ADAPTATION

8.1 Introduction

Over the past five decades there has been a rise in global temperatures of approximately 0.4°C at the earths surface. It is generally accepted that the main cause of this is the increase in greenhouse gases that are discharged into the atmosphere as a result of human activities, most notably carbon dioxide.

There are two main approaches to dealing with climate change:

1. Reduce the emission of greenhouse gases (reducing carbon emissions) in order to return the earths temperature variations to natural levels (mitigation).
2. Adapting to deal with the changes that will happen (adaptation).

Green roofs can benefit both the thermal performance of the buildings on which they are installed and the wider environment. As the implications of climate change become more pressing and better understood and as energy efficiency starts to become an integral element of building design, building professionals will have to look more closely at ways of adapting buildings to cope with higher and more extreme environmental temperatures, including improved insulation, thermal mass and urban heat island reduction.

Green roofs have a substantial thermal mass, a moderate insulation value and some cooling effect through evapotranspiration. These combined properties significantly reduce daily range of temperatures at the boundary between green roof and building structure.

Historically, these thermal properties were used as an important element in buildings such as icehouses (Figure 8.1), which in the UK were used from the 17th century until the introduction of the refrigerator to store ice. Fruit and vegetable stores were often covered with green roofs to help keep the contents cool.

Figure 8.1

A disused icehouse Sachsen bei Ansbach, Germany (courtesy P Early)

8.2 Thermal insulation

The thermal insulation provided by a green roof is often held up as one of its primary advantages. However, this should be understood in the context of the overall insulation strategy of a building. A green roof can be effective at providing insulation and thermal mass for lightweight poorly or non-insulated structures such as garages, sheds, industrial units, temporary buildings and existing flat roofed buildings, providing the structure can support the additional weight of the green roof.

Anecdotal information from a building services manager in London revealed that the application of a retrofitted green roof on a building had reduced the need for cooling/heating of industrial plant in the floor beneath. Since the green roof has been installed, cooling and heating fans have not been used and it is estimated that about 26 MW hours per year is being saved. Using current electricity rates this is approximately a £4300 saving per year (assuming 16p per kWh). A German green roofing manufacturer has estimated that green roofs can contribute to savings in fuel heating costs of two litres of fuel oil/m^2 of floor area/year in Germany.

It is unlikely that the figures for energy savings described above could be replicated for new buildings which meet the energy efficiency requirements of the Building Regulations, 2006. This is because the insulation layer now required ensures that the internal thermal performance is largely isolated from external environmental conditions. For buildings meeting the latest standards the amount of energy lost through the roof is very low compared to older buildings (roofs should meet a maximum U-value of 0.16 W/m^2K). In the hot, summer conditions found in Athens, Greece, the seasonal energy savings from adding a green roof were found to be only two per cent for a roof with an initial U-value of 0.4 W/m^2K. This is a much lower specification than that required by Building Regulations (Yannas *et al*, 2006). It shows that the insulation performance of the existing roof is very poor for a green roof to have any significant beneficial effect. Green roofs should not be used to reduce the conventional insulation layer of existing or new buildings.

The green roof should be considered as an addition to the existing or planned insulation, not as a replacement. Green roofs will have negligible thermal insulation value on new buildings that are already highly insulated. The refurbishment of an existing roof to provide a green roof is the ideal time to incorporate either more insulation under the waterproof layer, or to create an inverted roof where the green roof provides the ballast for a layer of insulation above the waterproofing. Where the green roof is to be used with an inverted roof, cold bridging is less likely to occur at the insulation joints. This is because of the reduced temperature gradient within a green roof compared to standard ballast, such as gravel or paving slabs.

8.3 Reduction of daily temperature fluctuations

Typically the roof of a building will heat up during the day and cool down at night. The diurnal temperature range is the difference between the minimum and maximum temperature when measured over a 24 hour period.

The diurnal temperature range for the waterproof layer of a conventionally constructed warm roof can be very large. Conventional roofs, and particularly dark coloured bitumen-covered roofs, absorb a large proportion of the incoming solar radiation and heat up considerably during the day. For example, the surface of a typical bitumen waterproof layer may exceed 35°C during a sunny summer's day, while falling to just above 0°C at night (Figure 8.2). A roof with a low level of insulation below the waterproof layer will allow the space below to heat up quickly in hot, sunny weather. The increased internal temperatures in the floor below the roof contribute to making the internal building environment uncomfortable for the buildings occupants. Overheating can lead to increased use of air-conditioning, which in turn will lead to increased energy consumption. During cold weather, the opposite effect occurs (Figure 8.3), resulting in a demand for extra heating of the floor directly below the roof and, again, increased energy consumption. The energy used for heating and cooling has financial as well as environmental implications.

Unlike a conventional roof, a green roof is a living system that reacts to the environment in a number of important ways:

- **evapotranspiration** from the plants and substrate uses a considerable proportion of the incoming solar radiation compared with non-green roof
- the green roof has a **large thermal mass**, which stores energy and delays the transfer of heat to or from the building fabric
- plants **absorb solar radiation** for photosynthesis
- plants have a **higher equivalent albedo** (solar radiation reflectivity) than many standard roof surfaces.

The diurnal temperature range at the waterproof layer of a green roof is much less than that of a conventional roof; it is typically below 10°C during summer for an extensive green roof (Figure 8.2). The diurnal temperature range will reduce with increasing substrate depth. The green roof protects the waterproof layer both from temperature changes and UV light that disrupts the chemical bonds in the waterproof layer materials. It also protects the waterproof layer from puncture by, for example, people walking on it. All these factors result in green roofs extending the life of the waterproof layer.

For a green roof, a much smaller proportion of incoming solar radiation is converted into heat than is the case for a conventional roof and so less heat is transferred to the wider environment. This is an important factor affecting the local urban microclimate (see Section 8.4).

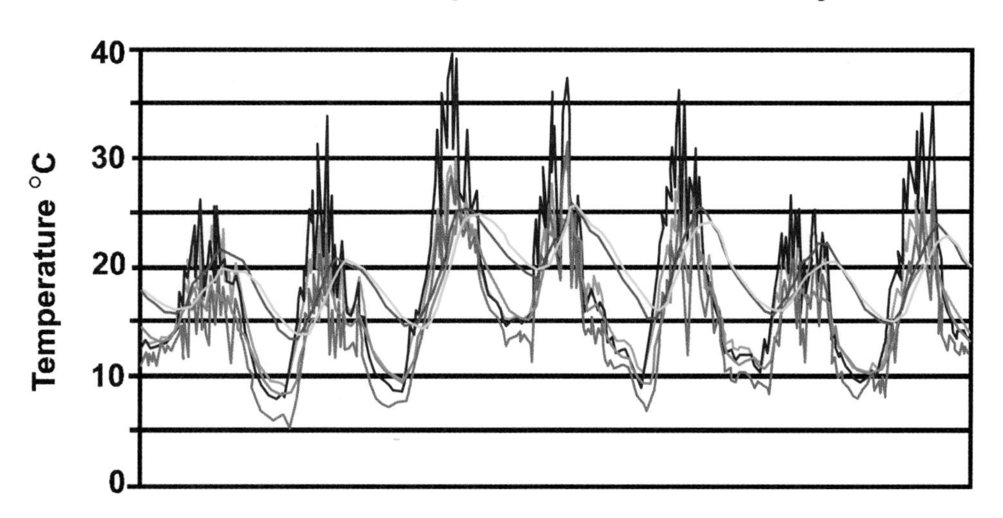

Figure 8.2 *Temperature at the roof surface and at the waterproof layer during summer showing diurnal variations (general trends taken from data by Koehler)*

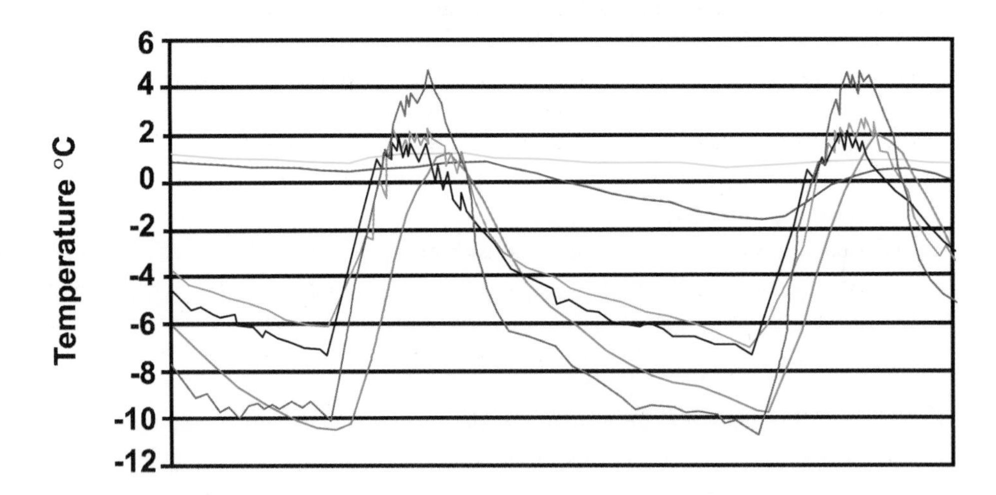

Figure 8.3 *Temperature at the roof surface and at the waterproof layer during winter showing diurnal variations (general trends taken from data by Koehler)*

8.4 Mitigation of the urban heat island effect

Urban areas have a higher average temperature than surrounding rural areas; this difference in temperatures is called the urban heat island effect. There is growing concern about the increased temperatures experienced in urban areas and how this is likely to get worse in the future as a result of climate change. An increase in the urban heat island effect can lead to greater air-born pollution and to increased use of air conditioning.

The cause of the heat island effect is a complex combination of factors that include the following (Santamouris, 2001):

- reduction of evaporating surfaces – more energy turned into sensible heat and less into latent heat
- thermal properties of materials – increased storage of sensible heat in building fabric
- anthropogenic heat released – from combustion of fuels and metabolism of animals/people
- canyon radiative effect – decrease of long-wave radiation lost to the sky and retained in the urban area due to radiation interchange between especially tall buildings within relatively narrow streets (otherwise known as "canyons") and reduction of albedo due to multiple reflection of short-wave radiation between building (or "canyon") surfaces
- urban greenhouse effect – increase of long-wave radiation reflected from the polluted, warmer urban atmosphere
- reduced turbulent heat transfer – transfer of heat to the air is reduced due to less air turbulence in streets.

There are two widely recognised and documented methods for reducing the heat island. The first, is to introduce more vegetation into the urban environment to provide shading and cooling through evapotranspiration and the second is to increase the reflectiveness (or albedo) of roofs. Roofs can be covered with lighter coloured or reflective materials that reflect a higher proportion of the received solar radiation back to the sky (a higher albedo) and hence produce less "sensible" heat.

Green roofs combine these approaches and are increasingly being proposed as mitigation for the urban heat island effect, especially in the USA. However, it is recognised that, to have a substantial effect, the area of green roofs in an urban area would have to be substantial.

Green roofs have been found to have a high equivalent albedo of between 0.7 and 0.85 depending upon the availability of water for evapotranspiration (Gaffin, 2005), which is similar to the range of the highest albedo roofing materials. Maintenance of the high albedo surface of conventional roofing materials, such as periodic cleaning is not required for green roofs.

Evaporative cooling on green roofs works by increasing humidity and reducing the amount of energy available for conversion into sensible heat. The largely dry summers of the UK climate result in a reduction of the real evapotranspiration rate compared to the theoretical potential evapotranspiration rate. In the most extreme circumstances, where there is no substrate moisture and hence little evapotranspiration, the vegetation will suffer drought stress and possibly die back providing little or no evapotranspiration benefit.

Wetland green roofs (ie those that are deliberately saturated with water) avoid this issue by their nature, but green roofs that are primarily specified for their climate altering properties will need the soil moisture to be retained at a level that allows evapotranspiration to continue at or near the potential rate. In this case it is likely that seasonal irrigation may be required to keep soil moisture at the required level. This may seem a contradiction to the idea of reducing energy consumption through the use of a green roof. However, the embodied energy of even potable water is low compared to the energy converted from solar radiation to specific latent heat for the evapotranspiration process. The use of irrigation carries an additional cost for equipment, installation, maintenance and operation and will fundamentally alter the roof growing conditions. In the UK it will also use increasingly scarce water resources, which should be avoided. Other preferred ways of maintaining moisture content of the substrate include increasing substrate depth and the inclusion of water retention features within the green roof build up.

The Toronto study discussed in Chapter 2 estimated that the widespread implementation of green roofs in the city would lead to a 0.5–2.0 degree reduction in local ambient temperatures, thus reducing both the need for air conditioning use and the air-born pollutants associated with the urban heat island effect. Table 8.1 is from the report and highlights the potential savings of energy by using a green roof. The report states that a major green roof implementation programme within the city could lead to a reduction in peak demand worth $68.7 million.

Table 8.1 *Potential direct savings from green roof implementation (Banting et al, 2005)*

Category of energy saving	Energy saving per sq m of green roof
Energy savings	4.15 kWh/sq m/year
Demand load reduction from direct energy production	0.0023 kW/sq m/year

The urban heat island effect will continue to increase as climate change results in higher temperatures, combined with the continual spread of hard, dark, impervious surfaces that are associated with urban expansion. Increasing urban temperatures compromise the passive cooling of existing buildings and its use in new buildings.

Further information is provided in the summary of research in Appendix 5.

8.5 Other benefits related to thermal performance

Green roofs can be used in a number of innovative ways to save energy by harnessing the beneficial effects of evapotranspiration. The Possman Cider Company, Frankfurt, Germany uses a wetland type green roof to collect and store rainwater that is used for cooling in the cider fermenting process. The rainwater is recycled and pumped back to the roof where it provides cooling to the building and is then used again. The annual saving in cooling costs is about £4000 and there is a saving in costs for plant and rainwater drainage fees (Earth Pledge, 2005).

Green roofs can improve the performance of photovoltaics panels (PVs) that are used to convert sunlight to electricity. The panels are less efficient when they heat up in strong sunlight. Research in Germany has shown that mounting PVs on green roofs improves their efficiency because evapotranspiration reduces the PVs temperature. The shading from the PVs provides a green roof with a variety of habitats from open sun to full shade which increases biodiversity. Not only do green roofs offer performance advantages for the PVs, they can also act as inexpensive ballast for typical PV supports, avoiding the need to penetrate the waterproof layer to secure the supports to the roof (Case study 10).

Case study 10 Messe Hall, Basel, Switzerland

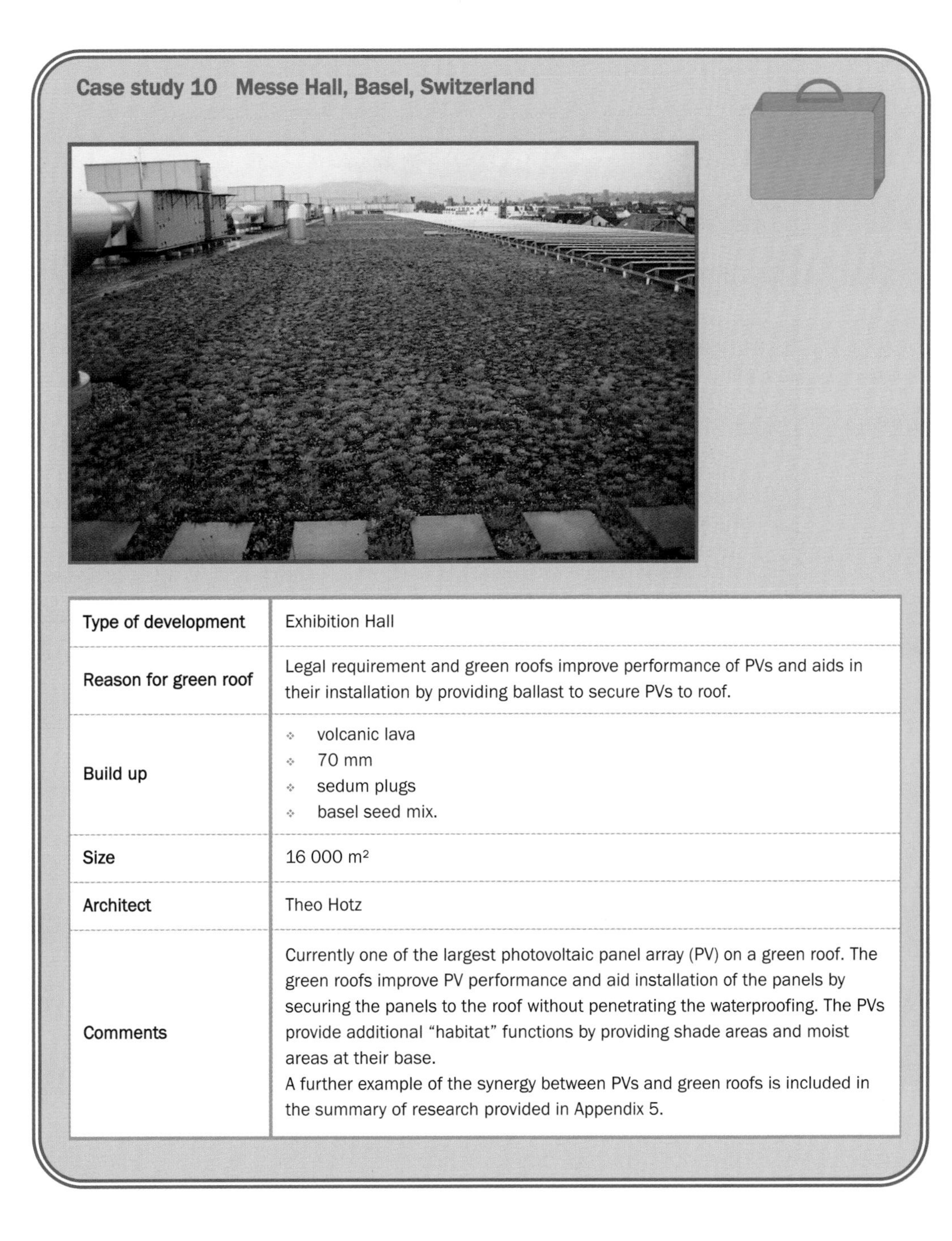

Type of development	Exhibition Hall
Reason for green roof	Legal requirement and green roofs improve performance of PVs and aids in their installation by providing ballast to secure PVs to roof.
Build up	- volcanic lava - 70 mm - sedum plugs - basel seed mix.
Size	16 000 m²
Architect	Theo Hotz
Comments	Currently one of the largest photovoltaic panel array (PV) on a green roof. The green roofs improve PV performance and aid installation of the panels by securing the panels to the roof without penetrating the waterproofing. The PVs provide additional "habitat" functions by providing shade areas and moist areas at their base. A further example of the synergy between PVs and green roofs is included in the summary of research provided in Appendix 5.

Benefits of green roofs for climate change mitigation and adaption: Key points

- the green roof is a living system that reacts to the environment in a number of ways:
  - evapotranspiration uses a large proportion of the incoming solar radiation
  - the green roof has a large thermal mass
  - plants absorb solar radiation for photosynthesis
  - plants have a higher equivalent albedo (solar radiation reflectivity) than many standard roof surfaces
- a green roof should be considered as an addition to the existing or planned insulation, not as a replacement. Green roofs can be effective at providing insulation and thermal mass for light weight poorly or non-insulated structures
- the diurnal temperature range at the waterproof layer of a green roof is much less than that of a conventional roof and will reduce with increasing substrate depth. The green roof protects the waterproof layer from temperature changes and UV light. It also protects the waterproof layer from puncture and all these factors can result in green roofs significantly extending the life of the waterproof layer
- green roofs are increasingly being proposed as mitigation for the urban heat island effect, especially in the USA. To have a substantial effect, however, the area of green roofs in an urban area would have to be substantial. Widespread implementation of green roofs in a city could reduce both the need for air conditioning and the air-born pollutants associated with the urban heat island effect
- green roofs can be used in a number of innovative ways to save energy by harnessing the beneficial effects of evapotranspiration. For example, green roofs can improve the performance of photovoltaic panels that are used to convert sunlight to electricity.

9 GREEN ROOF COMPONENTS AND PLANT COMMUNITIES

9.1 Components

The green roof system requires a minimum of four components:

- the root barrier
- the drainage layer (including geotextile filter above)
- the substrate (or growing medium)
- the vegetation layer.

Further components can be added depending on the specification or the particular system manufacturer, including filter membranes, moisture mats, protection boards, water retention systems, irrigation systems, special features to locate trees (eg anchorage fixings), and additional thermal insulation.

A cross-section highlighting the components of a typical commercial green roof system is shown in Figure 9.1, with further information on each of the key components provided in Sections 9.1.1 to 9.1.4. It should be noted that the drainage and substrate layers are the major elements by volume and account for the majority of the mass of a green roof.

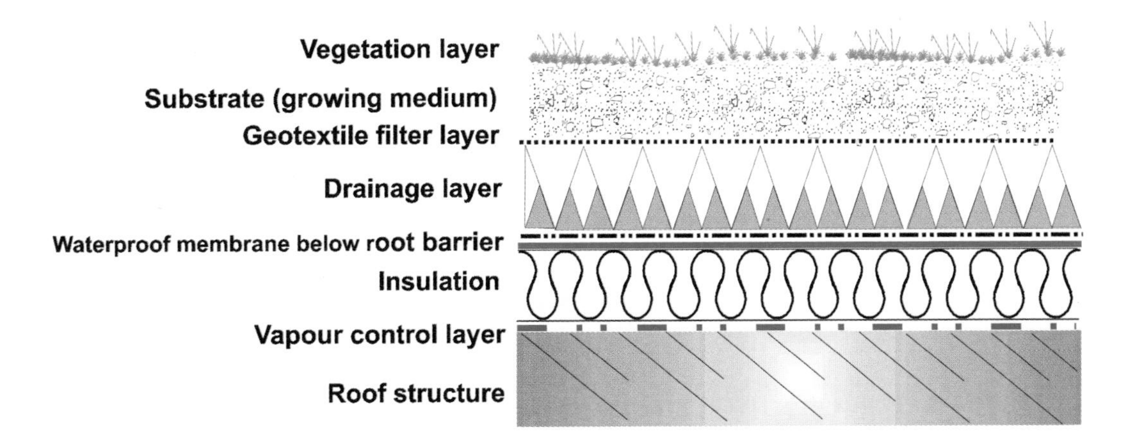

Figure 9.1 *Typical commercial green roof cross-section on warm roof*

9.1.1 Root barrier

The root barrier is an essential part of the system. It prevents the roots of vigorous plant species penetrating through to the waterproofing and damaging the membrane. Root barriers can be provided within the waterproofing in the form of a biocide, or they can be applied on top of waterproofing using a copper or heavy grade polythene-based material. The type of root membrane will vary depending on the system and the type of plants to be used. The type of root barrier is usually specified by the waterproofing supplier as they normally provide a guarantee for the system. On an inverted warm roof the root barrier needs to be below the insulation layer to avoid forming a vapour barrier above the insulation (see Figure 5.6, Chapter 5).

9.1.2 Drainage layer

The purpose of the drainage layer is, in combination with the substrate, to control the water retention properties of the green roof. Provision of a drainage layer gives three main benefits if properly specified:

1. It reduces the risk of water ponding on the roof. This is particularly important for flat roof constructions, which are more susceptible to failure if surface water ponding occurs for prolonged periods of time.
2. It maintains the correct drainage conditions needed to allow the desired plant species to survive and flourish. If the green roof system is too free-draining then plants may die back during rain-free periods. Conversely if the roof has insufficient drainage it may become waterlogged, which if it occurs for extended periods can cause plants to rot. If the correct water retention properties are not met for a particular vegetation type then other less desirable plant species (or none at all) may colonise the roof.
3. It controls the amount and timing of rainfall runoff and can contribute to the management of stormwater runoff. In central Europe a common reason for installing a green roof is to help meet planning or regulatory constraints that require controlled runoff from a development.

A geotextile filter layer (also known as the filter sheet or separation layer) should be included between the growing substrate and the drainage layer. The filter layer is a geotextile material that prevents fine particles from the growing substrate migrating to the drainage layer where they can disrupt the desired drainage properties. However, the filter layer does not prevent penetration of the drainage layer by plant roots, so the drainage layer can be utilised by plants in addition to the substrate.

Careful consideration needs to be given to the design of the drainage layer, taking into account local climate conditions and the desired water retention characteristics.

Drainage layers can be divided into two main categories:

1. Granular materials include sand and gravel, lava and pumice, expanded clay and slate as well as recycled materials such as foamed glass, power station clinker, crushed brick and roof tiles.
2. Modular systems comprise rectangular tiles that are placed side by side to form a continuous layer over the roof.

Sheet systems are often geocomposites and usually delivered in rolls (the width and length depends on the type of material). Both systems generally use profiled or dimpled sheets of plastic as reservoirs to hold water, with cross drainage for excess water. Both types may be combined to form a drainage layer.

Table 9.1 provides typical thicknesses and saturated weights of some materials that have been used as drainage layers in green roofs.

Table 9.1 *Drainage material physical properties (Kolb and Schwarz, 1999)*

Material	Typical thickness (mm)	Weight when saturated kg/m²
Plastic tiles	25	15
❖ with filling	40	20
❖ with 2–8 mm burnt clay	60	25
Foam tiles	50-65	2-2.5
Foam tiles profiled	75	25
❖ with filling	100	35
❖ with 2–8 mm burnt clay	140	50
Foam beads with polyethylene layer	30	6
Foam beads with polyurethane layer	35	25
Gravel	per 100	150–180
Sand and gravel	per 100	150–180
Lava*	per 100	120–140
Pumice*	per 100	80–120
Burnt clay (large pieces)	per 100	50–70
Burnt clay (small pieces)	per 100	60–80
Recycled ceramic tiles	per 100	110–130
Clinker (from coal burning)	per 100	90–110
Foamed glass	per 100	25–35

Note: Lava and pumice are not commonly available in the UK.

The more complicated drainage systems may incorporate a moisture mat that absorbs excess water, making it available during drier periods. If the load capacity of the roof is sufficient, it may be more cost effective to increase the depth of substrate and drainage layers of a simple system to increase the water retention properties rather than implement a complex multi-layered solution.

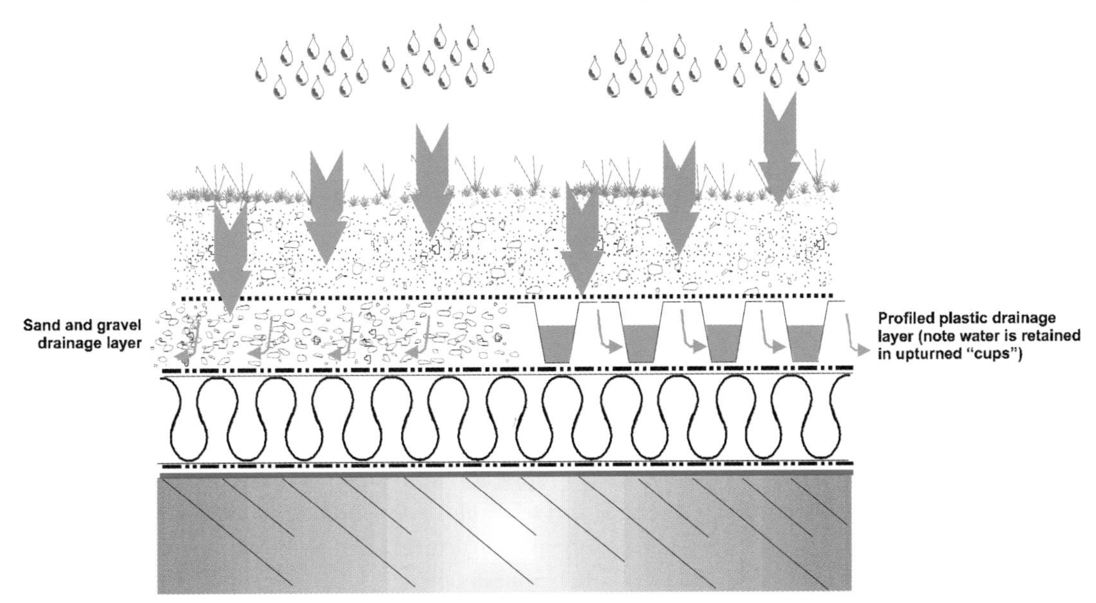

Figure 9.2 *Typical examples of drainage systems*

Introduction and background
Green roofs
Green walls
Nest boxes and other features
Appendices
Glossary, Abbreviations, References

Figure 9.3 *Profiled plastic drainage layer sheet (courtesy P Early)*

On a small roof drainage to the roof eaves and drains can be achieved by providing a perimeter zone where growing substrate is excluded. On larger roofs it may be necessary to implement a more complicated system including cross drainage. In all cases roof drainage points for runoff should be detailed so as to prevent blockage and ensure efficient operation (Figure 9.4)

Flat roofs should generally be laid to a minimum gradient of 1:60. This is particularly important when designing green roofs to minimise the risk of water ponding in the drainage layer. There are some proprietary systems available that allow green roofs to be installed with zero gradients.

Figure 9.4
Drainage point (courtesy P Early)

9.1.3 Substrate or growing medium layer

The purpose of the substrate layer is to provide the mechanical strength, open pore structure, nutrients, chemical composition and drainage properties that the desired plant species require.

The plant communities typical of intensive green roofs (ie similar to parks and gardens) require a deep and fertile growing medium, primarily topsoil. Maintenance requirements are increased by the use of fertile growing mediums, both to ensure the establishment of the desired species (ie through weeding) and to ensure that nutrient requirements continue to be met (ie through the application of fertiliser). Topsoil is also relatively dense and heavy when saturated, so significant loads should be accommodated by the roof structure. Load and maintenance requirements are generally an accepted part of intensive roof design.

In contrast, extensive roofs are often implemented in situations where weight and maintenance requirements are key design constraints. As a result lightweight substrates with low nutrient content are generally used. The low nutrient content, impacts on the variety of plant species that can be used, but importantly reduces the maintenance required to control invasive and aggressive plant species. The growing substrate can consist of a variety of materials and can exclude organic matter altogether. If organic matter, such as compost, is included, while good for water retention, it should be fully decomposed otherwise decomposition will further reduce the already low nitrogen content of the substrate (Kolb and Schwarz, 1999).

The use of peat should always be avoided as it leads to the depletion of biodiversity interest in the areas from which it is extracted.

Green roof substrates can be made up to suit particular vegetation types or microclimates, and can be distributed on a roof at varying depths in order to provide varied habitats for plants and invertebrates. The substrate may be layered to mimic more closely the strata found in natural soil systems.

Care should be taken when storing, transporting or mixing substrates as damage to their pore structure can have a negative impact on plant growth. A typical substrate has a pore volume of 60–70 per cent (35–45 per cent water, 15–25 per cent air) and 30–40 per cent solid particles (Johnston and Newton, 2004). It is also important to ensure that the substrates used do not include pollutants that could leach out in the runoff from the roof and pollute watercourses (see Chapter 7). Descriptions of typical substrates are given in Table 9.2 and some typical physical properties are given in Table 9.3.

Table 9.2 ***Common materials used for the green roof growing substrate layer (Kolb and Schwarz, 1999)***

Vegetation substrate	Thickness (mm)	Weight when saturated (kg/m²)
Treated top soil for intensive green roof	100	150–200
Open pore substrate for intensive green roof	100	100–130
Open pore substrate for extensive green roof, high density (lava, recycled roof tile)	100	140–180
Open pore substrate for extensive green roof, low density (burnt clay)	100	80–130
Layered mix (pumice, burnt clay)	100	70–100

Table 9.3 Typical growing substrate layer physical properties (adapted from Kolb and Schwarz, 1999)

Material	Origin	Availability	Weight	Moisture retention	Nutrient content/ retention	Stability
Sand	Naturally occurring	Abundant		Fine sand can become saturated if drainage is poor. Coarse sand can be too free-draining		Stable
Lava and Pumice[1]	Naturally occurring	Limited (not quarried in the UK)	Lightweight			
Gravel	Naturally occurring	Abundant	Heavy			
Subsoil	Naturally occurring	Often readily available on-site	Heavy		Low nutrient content	
Perlite	Manufactured					Particles tend to collapse over time
Vermiculite	Manufactured		Very lightweight	Poor	Poor	Particles tend to collapse over time
Expanded clay and slate	Manufactured		Lightweight	High		
Rockwool[2]	Manufactured		Very lightweight	Poor	Poor	
Crushed brick tiles	Recycled			Some	Some	Stable and uniform
Brick rubble[3]	Recycled	Often readily available on-site		Some	Some	Stable and uniform
Crushed concrete	Recycled	Often readily available on-site		Poor	Poor	Stable

1 Lava and pumice are not commonly available in the UK.

2 High embodied energy.

3 Residual mortar and cement will increase alkalinity and impact on the choice of plant.

Figure 9.5 *Cross-section through the simple but successful extensive green roof covering the Moos Reservoirs, Zurich, Switzerland (courtesy P Early)*

9.1.4 Vegetation layer

There are four main methods of establishing vegetation on a green roof:

1. **Vegetation mats** provide 90–100 per cent vegetation cover immediately they are laid. However, they are the most expensive way of greening a roof. The mats should be installed quickly, without gaps, and secured until rooted so as not to be blown from the roof. Irrigation may also be required for a time (Kolb and Schwarz, 1999).
2. **Plug planting** is planting a pot grown plant directly into the substrate, allowing the easy mixing of plant species and the possibility to be creative. It may take time for the vegetation to reach a reasonable coverage, and irrigation may be required to establish the plants. Plug plants are vulnerable to being disturbed by birds searching for invertebrates.
3. **Seeds and cuttings** can be hand distributed, which can be a cost effective, although slow, method of achieving vegetation cover. They can be sprayed onto a roof in a gel or hydromulch that is designed to hold the seeds in place until the plants become established, this is particularly useful for sloping roofs where the seeds would otherwise wash off. Birds again may pull plants up before they can become established and irrigation may be necessary (Kolb and Schwarz, 1999).
4. **Natural colonisation** (allowing a bare substrate to colonise naturally) will provide a plant community that is in sympathy with its local environment. This is likely to be the cheapest and most environmentally and ecologically beneficial way of vegetating a green roof. However, the client should be aware that the aesthetic properties of the roof are less predictable and the final result may not appear as attractive as a green roof that has resulted from intentional planting.

The choice of vegetation will affect the loads imposed on the roof (Table 9.4).

Table 9.4 *Typical vegetation weight (Kolb and Schwarz, 1999)*

Vegetation	Depth of substrate (mm)	Typical weight (vegetation only) (kg/m^2)
Extensive green roof of grasses, moss, sedum etc	50–100	10
Extensive green roof of soil covering plants and small shrubs below 0.5 m	100–150	15
Intensive green roof of larger plants and small shrubs below 1 m	150–200	20
Intensive green roof of larger plants and small shrubs below 3 m	200–400	30
Intensive green roof of large plants and small trees below 6 m	400–1000	60
Intensive green roof of large plants and small trees below 10 m	1000+	150

Figure 9.6 *A very simple, inexpensive and successful green roof construction for a farmyard barn in Switzerland, using materials found on the farm (drainage layer is made of reeds, the growing substrate is local soil and gravel) (courtesy S Wilson)*

9.2 Plant communities

Intensive and simple intensive green roofs can incorporate a range of plants that are well suited to deep fertile soil. They satisfy the aspirations of clients who want a green roof that resembles a garden. Extensive green roofs are designed to encourage a wide variety of wild plants that can survive under more stressful conditions. Those species that are introduced, or that occur naturally, will have to have some tolerance to drought and nutrient poor substrates.

The physical and chemical properties of the substrate to be used and local environment conditions should be considered when choosing the type of plant community. Aspect, shading and the combination of rainfall patterns and substrate drainage properties will have a considerable influence on the type of plant community that will flourish on a particular roof.

The following categories of plant are typically found on green roofs:

- mosses and ferns
- herbaceous perennials
- annuals
- grasses
- trees and shrubs
- bulbs.

9.2.1 Mosses and ferns

Mosses comprise some very resilient species that can survive in harsh, nutrient poor, conditions (Figure 9.7). Ferns, while less common on extensive green roofs, nevertheless can withstand similarly harsh conditions, although generally shade is required.

Figure 9.7 *Moss growing on an asbestos cement roof in Lewes, Sussex (courtesy P Early)*

9.2.2 Herbaceous perennials

Many native species in the UK are appropriate as green roof plants, especially those species associated with dry grasslands, cliffs, dunes and shingle habitat. The choice of plants will largely depend on the depth and type of substrate. Table 9.5 gives an indication of suitable native species and the depths of substrate that they require (Dunnett, 2006).

Extensive green roofs are often associated with succulent species, in particular sedums and house-leeks *Sempervivum spp.* which can tolerate dry and nutrient poor environments. They are the typical plant cover of many off-the-shelf extensive green roof systems. On some roofs sedums have become established in place of turf because it was too dry in the summer for the grass to survive (Figure 9.8).

Figure 9.8

Sedums and mosses have replaced the original turf (courtesy P Early)

Sedums can also provide significant visual interest. The different coloured flowers and foliage of sedums can add colour to a roof during the summer. Sedums generally provide a lush green carpet, but may turn red when stressed by heat or drought. It should be noted that sedums are unlikely to survive on poorly drained roofs.

As the substrate depth increases, so to does the range of herbaceous perennials able to survive on the green roof. Various species of Thymus, Alyssum, Campanula and Potentilla can be introduced when the depth exceeds 60 mm (Dunnett, 2006), which add further variety of colour throughout the flowering season.

Table 9.5 *Native or naturalised plant species suitable for use on green roofs*

Key

Best substrate depth | Suitable substrate depth | Unlikely to succeed

			Substrate depth			
			Extensive roofs		Semi-extensive roofs	
Species name	Common name	Habitat	20–50 mm	50–100 mm	100–150 mm	150–200 mm
Calcareous grasslands						
Clinopodiun acinos	Basil thyme	Calcareous grasslands				
Campanula glomerata	Clustered bellflower	Calcareous grasslands				
Centaurea scabiosa	Greater knapweed	Calcareous grasslands				
Clinopodium vulgare	Wild basil	Calcareous grasslands				
Erigeron acer	Blue fleabane	Calcareous grasslands				
Galium verum	Lady's bedstraw	Calcareous grasslands				
Echium vulgare	Viper's bugloss	Calcareous grasslands				
Helianthemum nummularium	Rockrose	Calcareous grasslands				
Hypericum perforatum	St John's wort	Calcareous grasslands				
Leontodon hispidus	Rough hawkbit	Calcareous grasslands				
Linum catharticum	Fairy flax	Calcareous grasslands				
Origanum vulgare	Marjoram	Calcareous grasslands				
Primula vulgaris	Cowslip	Calcareous grasslands				
Pulsatilla vulgaris	Pasqueflower	Calcareous grasslands				
Sanguisorba minor	Salad burnet	Calcareous grasslands				
Scabiosa columbaria	Small scabious	Calcareous grasslands				
Teucrium chamaedrys	Wall germander	Calcareous grasslands				
Veronica spicata	Spiked speedwell	Calcareous grasslands				
Dry grassland and grassland						
Achillea millefolium	Yarrow	Dry grasslands				
Campanula rotundifolia	Harebell	Dry grasslands				
Dianthus deltoids	Maiden pink	Sandy grasslands				
Echium vulgare	Viper's bugloss	Dry grasslands				

Table 9.5 *Native or naturalised plant species suitable for use on green roofs (contd)*

Species name	Common name	Habitat	Substrate depth: Extensive roofs 20–50 mm	Substrate depth: Extensive roofs 50–100 mm	Substrate depth: Semi-extensive roofs 100–150 mm	Substrate depth: Semi-extensive roofs 150–200 mm
Galium saxatile	Heath bedstraw	Acid grasslands				
Geranium molle	Dove's-foot cranesbill	Dry grasslands				
Hieraceum aurantiacum	Orange hawkbit	Dry grasslands				
Pilosella officinarum	Mouse-ear hawkweed	Grasslands				
Knautia arvensis	Field scabious	Dry grasslands				
Leontodon autumnalis	Autumn hawkbit	Grasslands				
Leucanthemum vulgare	Ox-eye daisy	Grasslands				
Linaria vulgaris	Common toadflax	Grasslands				
Lotus corniculatus	Bird's foot trefoil	Dry grasslands				
Potentilla erecta	Tormentil	Acid grasslands				
Thymus drucei	Wild thyme	Dry grasslands				
Thymus serpyllum	Breckland thyme	Sandy heaths, dry grasslands				
Other habitats						
Armeria maritime	Thrift	Cliffs, rocks				
Campanula rotundifolia	Harebell	Heaths, dunes				
Echium vulgare	Viper's bugloss	Sand, shingle				
Erodium cicutarium	Common storksbill	Dunes, cliffs, sand				
Hieraceum aurantiacum	Orange hawkbit	Banks				
Linum catharticum	Fairy flax	Dunes, rocks				
Prunella vulgaris	Self heal	Disturbed ground, grassland				
Sedum album	White stonecrop	Walls, rocks, cliffs				
Sedum acre	Biting stonecrop	Old walls and roofs				
Sedum reflexum	Reflexed stonecrop	Rocks, wall, dry banks				
Silene maritim	Sea campion	Shingle, cliffs, mountains				
Teucrium chamaedrys	Wall germander	Old walls				
Veronica spicata	Spiked speedwell	Rocks				

9.2.3 Grasses

Traditional houses in northern Europe used turf as part of their roof construction (Figure 9.9). On the shallow substrates of a modern extensive green roof (<100 mm) only a thin scattering of grasses will survive, but as substrate depth increases, so will the grass cover. Grasses can be used to provide visual/structural interest, to provide a matrix within which other plants such as meadow flowers can become established or to provide a walking surface (sward). If a sward is to be created tough, regenerating species should be planted and a semi-intensive roof type will be required (Dunnett and Kingsley, 2004). A roof lawn will require a significant amount of maintenance input to retain its aesthetic qualities.

Figure 9.9

Traditional turf roof on a house in Rackwick, Hoy, Orkney Islands (courtesy P Early)

9.2.4 Trees and shrubs

Trees and shrubs may be grown on intensive roofs that have sufficient substrate depth to support them (see Table 9.6). Significant maintenance and irrigation is required to retain the appearance of such roofs (Figure 9.10). Other considerations will include root penetration, structural loading, management related issues and health and safety – wind blow on a roof could have disastrous consequences. Trees should have a suitable anchorage to resist being blown off the roof.

Figure 9.10 *Trees and shrubs growing on the intensive roof covering Canary Wharf underground station, London (courtesy P Early)*

9.2.5 Bulbs

Bulbs can be grown in green roof substrates provided the depth is sufficient (see Table 9.6). Bulbs of *Allium spp.*, a member of the onion family, are one of the most popular varieties to grow on a green roof.

Table 9.6 ***Relationship between substrate depth and typical plant communities (Dunnett and Kingsbury, 2004)***

Substrate depth (mm)	Typical plant types
0-50	Sedum/moss
50-100	Small bulbs, dry meadow, low growing drought tolerant perennials, grasses and alpines
100-200	Small shrubs, lawn and turf grass, semi-extensive mixtures of low to medium dry habitat perennials, grasses and alpines
200-500	Medium sized shrubs, edible plants, general perennials and grasses
500+	Small deciduous and coniferous trees

9.2.6 Annuals

Self seeding annuals with a tolerance for drought can be successful on extensive green roofs, adding a dash of colour. Examples include scarlet pimpernel *Anagallis arvensis*, scentless mayweed *Tripleurospermum inodorum*, poppys *Papaver spp.*, and wild mignonette *Reseda lutea*.

Green roof components and plant communities: Key points

- the green roof system requires a minimum of four components:
  1. The root barrier prevents roots from vigorous plant species damaging the waterproof membrane. Various forms of root barrier are available, including physical barriers (eg heavy grade polythene based material) and biocides.
  2. The drainage layer controls the water retention properties of the green roof. The drainage layer can be made from granular materials (eg gravel, stone chippings, crushed brick) or a proprietary system can be used (eg profiled plastic or geocomposite sheets).
  3. The substrate or growing medium provides the mechanical strength, open pore structure, nutrients, chemical composition and drainage properties required by the desired plant species. Substrates can range from nutrient rich topsoil to low nutrient granular materials (eg gravel).
  4. The vegetation layer provides the wildlife habitat and the aesthetic properties of the roof. Vegetation can be established by laying vegetation mats, by plug planting, by planting seeds and cuttings, or through natural colonisation.
- the drainage and substrate layers are the major elements by volume and account for the majority of the mass of a green roof
- roof drainage points should be detailed to prevent blockage and ensure efficient operation
- the physical and chemical properties of the substrate and local environment conditions should be considered when choosing the type of plant community
- categories of plant typically grown or found on green roofs include:
  - mosses, lichens and ferns – include some very resilient species that can survive in nutrient poor, conditions
  - herbaceous perennials – many native species in the UK are appropriate as green roof plants. Sedums are commonly used
  - annuals – those with a tolerance for drought can be successful on extensive green roofs, adding colour
  - grasses – can be used to provide structural interest, a matrix within which other plants such as meadow flowers can become established or to provide a walking surface (sward). Only a thin covering of grass will survive on shallow substrates
  - trees and shrubs – may be grown on intensive and simple intensive green roofs that have sufficient substrate depth to support them. Anything up to fully mature trees can be accommodated, but this type of roof will need significant maintenance and irrigation
  - bulbs – can be grown in extensive roof substrates provided the depth is sufficient.
- the choice of plant type is closely related to the substrate depth.

10 GREEN ROOF DESIGN CONSIDERATIONS

Clear objectives and design criteria should inform the design and construction of green roofs. The criteria should consider how the benefits for biodiversity and sustainable drainage can be maximised, as well as addressing climate change amenity, health and safety, and maintenance concerns. Careful consideration also needs to be given to the loading implications of the roof on the structure of the building and any restrictions on the design imposed by the pitch of the roof.

10.1 The design process

Flow charts showing the design and construction process for green roofs are provided in Figures 10.1 and 10.2. The first chart is for the overall process and the second covers the design process.

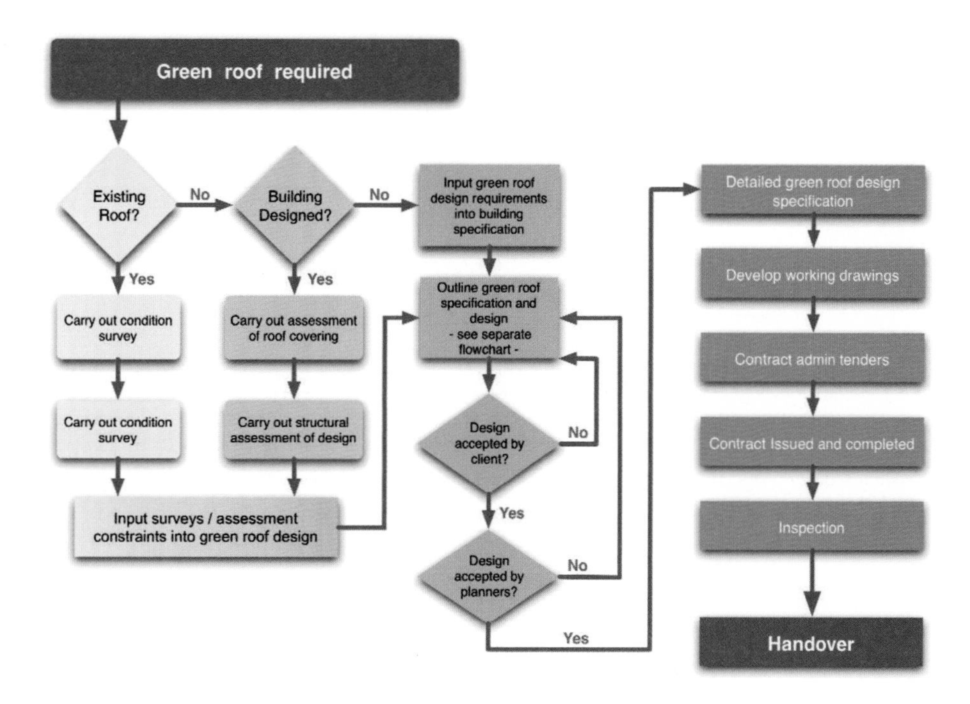

Figure 10.1 *Overall design and construction flow chart*

Introduction and background

Green roofs

Green walls

Nest boxes and other features

Appendices

Glossary, Abbreviations, References

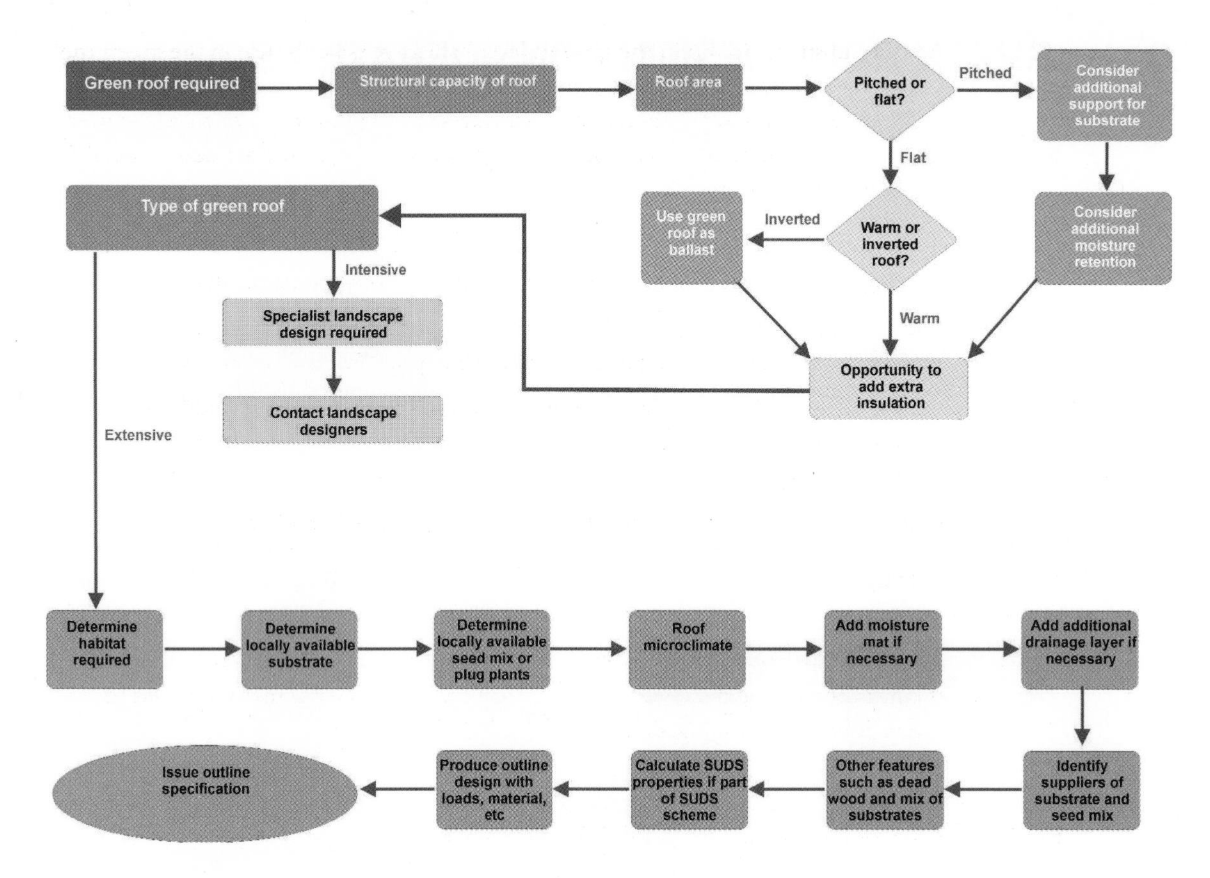

Figure 10.2 *Flow chart showing breakdown of design process*

10.2 Design for biodiversity

Where a green roof is being implemented to enhance biodiversity and to meet specific habitat or species objectives, the roof design and system used should be tailored to meet the specific circumstances of the site and local habitats. An off-the-shelf system may provide general benefit to wildlife, but it is unlikely to meet specific requirements. Where a commercial system is to be used it should be substrate based, that is where the blanket or the plugs are laid onto a growing medium.

Where a green roof is required to benefit a specific species or to provide specific habitat, a detailed assessment should be undertaken that considers the following points:

- feasibility and constraints
  - Will the area available provide meaningful habitat?
  - Does the roof structure limit the choice to lightweight systems or are there areas with greater structural support (eg above pillars) that will allow for the creation of substrate mounds to create a variety of habitats?
  - Is the roof area viewable and is it important that the roof is aesthetically pleasing and tidy (this may remove the option for natural colonisation)?
  - Will the height of the roof restrict its use by certain species?
  - Can habitat be created on the green roof that complements the wider landscape and biodiversity strategy for the area?
- types of substrates:
  - Would it be beneficial for the specific species of interest to use a variety of substrates in order to create a range of plant communities? This is particularly relevant in regard to the mitigation for loss of brownfield habitat.

- Are the substrates found in the ground level habitat suitable for use in the green roof system (eg weight) and will they support complementary objectives (eg stormwater management)? If not, are there other substrates available from site or manufactured, that broadly replicate the soil conditions at ground level, but that are better suited for use in green roof systems?

- the type of vegetation:
  - Will a generic system provide adequate provision of appropriate habitat?
  - Can a generic system be "supported" with an appropriate seed mix to allow the green roof to develop into a more diverse habitat while providing an instant green affect?
  - Does the green roof design require the use of wildflower seeds and wildflower plugs to produce the best habitat replication?
  - Will the green roof need to serve multiple habitat functions (eg foraging, nesting, shelter) or are some of these functions served by neighbouring habitats.
  - Would the species of interest benefit from areas of bare substrate?
- Other landscape features:
  - Would the species of particular interest benefit from micro-habitats created through the inclusion of boulders, logs and other features. This is particularly relevant in terms of brownfield mitigation.

The implementation of a successful biodiverse green roof requires a dynamic working relationship between ecologists, structural and civil engineers, landscape architects, horticulturalists and green roof system suppliers.

Figure 10.3 *A biodiverse semi-wetland roof under construction with the different substrates visible, Switzerland (courtesy P Early)*

Case study 11 Tesco, Sutton, London, UK

Type of development	Retail (supermarket)
Reason for green roof	Planning constraint for ecology
Type of green roof	Metal ridge
Build up	Capillary matting overlaid by locally sourced crushed brick/crushed concrete and a subsoil mix.
Planting	The vegetated layer is a pre-grown sedum blanket over seeded with a local provenance selected wildflower mix.
Size	1000 m²
Client	Tesco
Architects	BMD Architects
Main contractor	Kier
Green roof supplier	Greenfix Ltd
Comments	The light roof structure is unable to support a heavy subsoil build up so a light weight, low fertility organic layer was required. The roof is required to reduce peak time water runoff, but also to support a diverse culture of plant species to encourage invertebrates and birds etc. To encourage the long-term viability of species, mounds of growing medium (up to 300 mm) have been incorporated over the strong points of the roof.
Completion date	2006

Case study 12 Aberporth Cardigan, UK

Type of development	Industrial park
Reason for green roof	Blend development into the landscape
Type of green roof	Single Ply, warm roof industrial park
Build-up and planting	**Unit one:** ✧ natural mat system laid onto substrate ✧ proprietary system and substrate formulation ✧ height of system (waterproofing to substrate surface): 105 mm ✧ height of vegetation layer (above substrate surface, dependent upon season): 50 to 150 mm ✧ saturated weight of planted element: 95 kg per m^2 ✧ plant cover at installation: Minimum 95 % **Units two and seven:** ✧ mounded plug and hydro plant layer installation with wild flower seeding. Proprietary system and substrate formulation ✧ height of system (waterproofing to substrate surface): Mean 150 mm. Range 95 to 205 mm ✧ saturated weight of planted element: Mean 145 kg per m^2. Range 90–200 kg per m^2 ✧ other features included in system build up include locally sourced cut or fallen timber (nominal 50 to 100mm section diameter up to 2000 mm section length) and locally sourced shelter stones (nominal 400 mm maximum breadth) ✧ plant cover at installation: Approximately 5–10 %. 50–80 % established plant cover in nine to 12 months[1]. **Units three and four:** ✧ plug and hydro plant layer installation ✧ proprietary system and substrate formulation ✧ height of system (waterproofing to substrate surface): 105 mm ✧ height of vegetation layer (above substrate surface, dependent on season): 50–150 mm ✧ saturated weight of planted element: 95 kg per m^2 ✧ plant cover at installation: Approximately 5 %. 50–80 % established plant cover in nine to 12 months. 1 The client was advised that where the primary goal is to increase the biodiversity of the roof, achieving 100 % plant cover quickly should not be a prime concern.
Size	A total area of 2416 m^2, on curved roof with 0–10° pitch
Green roof supplier	Greenroof.co.uk

continued

Case study 12 Aberporth Cardigan, UK (contd)

Comments	The site located on the West Wales Coast. The designers and suppliers encouraged the developer to consider a diversity of roof coverings and to view the project as not just a site specific response to environmental concerns but as a standard bearer for future industrial development both within Wales and the UK. Issues that arose during the contract included: 1 Developing sustainable and diverse specifications and taking them to completion within the standard construction process. 2 Trafficking of finished system. 3 Level of understanding from the client and potential building users (eg discussions with client regarding how much stone and/or timber can be left as part of roof coverings. The "messy" appearance of two of the roofs may be discouraging to end users from taking up leases).
Completion date	2005

10.3 Design and specification for sustainable drainage

Green roofs provide interception storage by retaining the first 5 mm or more of a design rainfall event. Kellagher and Lauchlan (2005) have identified that, where interception storage is provided, the volume of attenuation storage can be reduced (and possibly long-term storage as well). So it is possible to allow for the attenuating effect of a green roof in the design of a SUDS scheme. Green roofs should even provide some contribution to attenuating rates of runoff from large events (the rate of runoff from the roof needs to be compared with the allowable discharge rate from the site) and this should be considered in sizing other parts of the drainage system. Even when saturated, the roof surface is rougher and thus the drainage route more tortuous than for a normal roof, and so the rate of runoff should still be reduced (see Appendix 3). The timing of the peak rate should also be delayed when compared to a normal roof.

A common way of designing green roofs for stormwater management is to simply allow a reduced runoff coefficient (the percentage of rainfall that turns into surface water running off the roof) when analysing single storm events. This approach is adopted in New Zealand (Auckland Regional Council, 2003) and Germany (Forschungsgesellschaft Landschaftsentwicklung Landschaftsbaue V, 2002).

German guidance on runoff coefficients from green roofs for single design events is summarised in Table 10.1. A set of runoff coefficients could be developed for use in the UK using the approach discussed by Miller (2006 and 2006a). In Germany, the standard design event for urban runoff management is 25 mm of rainfall falling in 15 minutes. This would be roughly equivalent to a 1 in 100 year return period event in the south east of England (15 min duration).

In comparison the volume of rainfall typically used in ground level SUDS design in the UK will vary from 51–82 mm for a 100-year return period, six hour duration event (in the South East and Midlands it varies between 60 and 70 mm). However, green roofs can be effective in managing runoff for events of this size (see Chapter 7).

Table 10.1 *Coefficient of discharge for green roofs (FLL, 2002)*

	Runoff coefficient (%)	
Roof construction	**Roof gradient up to 15°**	**Roof gradient greater than 15°**
Greater than 500 mm substrate depth	10	n/a
250–500 mm substrate depth	20	n/a
150–250 mm substrate depth	30	n/a
100–150 mm substrate depth	40	50
60–100 mm substrate depth	50	60
40–60 mm substrate depth	60	70
20–40 mm substrate depth	70	80

Note based on a design rainfall event of 25 mm of rainfall falling in 15 minutes This is equivalent to a 1 in 100-year return period event in the south east of England (15 min duration).

Factors that affect the water retention efficiency of green roofs are:

1 Storage capacity of the substrate and drainage layer (most significant).
2 Type of vegetation.
3 Degree of saturation of the substrate at any time.
4 Climatic factors (temperature, wind, evaporation rate).
5 Intensity and duration of rainfall.
6 Water requirements of plants.

An estimate of the annual runoff from a flat green roof can be obtained from the equation:

Yearly runoff (mm) = $(693 - 1.15R) + 0.45(R^2 - 8)D$ (Mentens *et al*, 2003)

Where: R = Annual rainfall in mm/yr and D = substrate thickness in cm.

This equation is based on experience in Western European climates and a lower % reduction may apply depending on rainfall intensity and duration. Similar equations could, however, be developed for the UK.

Green roofs will be most effective from a drainage point of view when they are combined with other SUDS components to form a stormwater management train (a series of drainage structures placed one after the other). An example of this has been constructed at Zurich railway station, where a green roof is connected to an infiltration basin (Figures 10.4 and 10.5).

Figure 10.4 *Infiltration basin at Zurich Station (courtesy S Wilson)*

Figure 10.5 *Green roof connected to an infiltration basin at Zurich Station (courtesy S Wilson)*

The potential reduction in downstream storage volume has been estimated for an example green roof with different runoff coefficients. The calculations have used the runoff coefficients for a green roof provided by FLL for different substrate thicknesses and assume 95 per cent runoff for a normal roof. The results are summarised in Figure 10.6 and show that the use of a green roof could potentially have a significant impact in reducing the requirement for downstream storage for the management of runoff. The precise reduction for any site will depend on a number of factors including the location and the drainage discharge limits for the site.

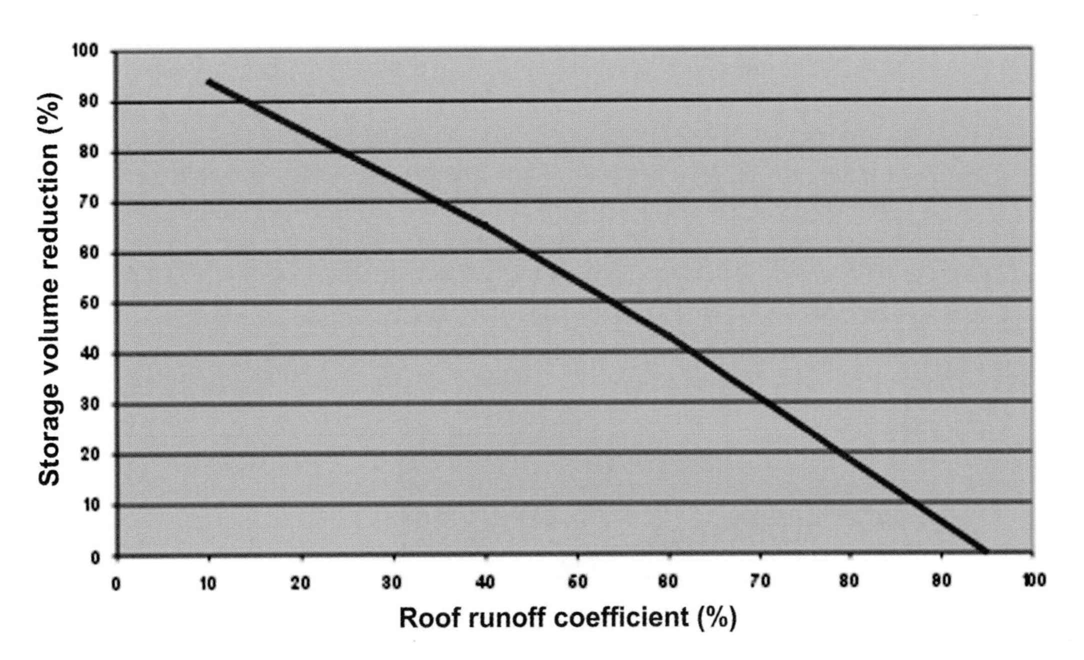

Figure 10.6 *Example of potential reduction of downstream storage volumes*

American experience suggests that the green roof peak rate of runoff can be less than or equal to the rate from a greenfield site for storm events with total volumes up to three times the maximum water retention capacity of the substrate (Pennsylvania Department of Environmental Protection, 2004). For example, if the substrate has a maximum water retention of 25 mm then the peak rate will be attenuated for storms with a rainfall volume of 75 mm. This needs to be considered against the roof construction and local rainfall characteristics.

The most important design aspect of green roofs in relation to stormwater management is the specification of the substrate and drainage layer and analysis of performance in a range of rainfall events. In particular, the specification should consider the:

- storage capacity of the substrate and drainage layer (most significant). This is determined by specifying the maximum water storage capacity of the substrate and drainage layer and considering the thickness of construction. This should be determined in accordance with the FLL guidelines (FLL, 2002)
- flow capacity or permeability of the drainage layer. This should be determined in accordance with the FLL guidelines (FLL, 2002)
- permeability of the substrate. This should be determined in accordance with the FLL guidelines (FLL, 2002)
- chemical composition of the substrate (it should not leach significant quantities of pollutants). Materials should meet the requirements of the Environment Agency Waste Acceptance Criteria for inert waste when tested in accordance with British Standard BS EN12457-3

- management regime – the use of fertilisers and herbicides should be avoided if pollution of runoff is of concern.

10.4 Slope limitations

The majority of green roofs are located on flat roofs, ie those with slopes or pitch of 10° or less from the horizontal (see Chapter 5). As the steepness of the slope increases so consideration of substrate depth, methods of substrate and water retention, and drainage become more important to prevent undue water stress and erosion. Typically, intensive green roofs are constructed on slopes of up to 5° and extensive roofs on slopes of up to 30°. Generally, the maximum slope for commonly available extensive green roof systems is 45°. However, there are examples where green roofs have been used at steeper angles. The steeper the slope, the greater the requirement for the green roof to incorporate a sub-frame or retention method which provides support and anchorage for the substrate and vegetation layer.

Figure 10.7

The pitched green roofs of the Hedgehog development, Brighton. This green roof has no additional structural support (courtesy P Early)

Green roofs can be adapted to many geometric forms, which, when coupled with imaginative design can result in unusual and spectacular buildings. Examples where green roofs have been used in this way include those designed by the Austrian artist Hundertwasser and by Swiss architect Peter Vetch (Figure 10.8).

Figure 10.8 *The nine house development at Lättenstrasse, Dietikon, Switzerland, designed by Architect Peter Vetch, shows that green roof design need not preclude creative building design (courtesy P Early)*

Figure 10.9 *Construction of green roof on a pitched roof (courtesy D Gedge)*

10.5 Structural issues

With an appropriate design, green roofs can be constructed on almost any rooftop waterproof layer, including concrete, steel, bitumen and wood, and can be incorporated in a wide variety of new build and retrofit situations.

In most cases the introduction of a green roof will have loading implications for the building. Any roof should be sufficiently engineered to carry the roof self-weight (including saturated green roof materials) and intermittent loads from wind, snow, and human access (repair, maintenance, amenity, means of escape) etc. These loads should be accommodated by the roof structure without undue distortion or damage to the building fabric (Harrison, 2000). The Building Regulations (1991) for England and Wales state:

> *The building shall be constructed so that the combined dead, imposed and wind loads are sustained and transmitted to the ground;*
>
> *a)* *Safely.*
>
> *b)* *Without causing such deflection or deformation of any part of the building, or such movement of the ground, as will impair the stability of any part of another building.*

A major design consideration for any green roof project is the combined green roof system weight. Typical weights for a range of drainage materials, substrates and vegetation types have already been described earlier in this section and these should be used to calculate the loads imposed by the green roof.

The actual loads applied to any single roof will be site, location and building configuration specific. For example, the geometry of a roof and the surrounding topography make a significant difference to the wind and snow loads. Each country of the UK has developed standards for the accommodation of loads within roof design.

A study into the benefits of, and barriers to, the implementation of green roofs in London noted that *"...of the engineers asked, 64 per cent disagreed that (structure) was [commonly] a constraint and 40 per cent of architects disagreed as well"*. Arguably, both these groups are in a better position than other stakeholder groups to assess the physical viability of green roofs (Ingleby, 2002).

Most buildings are designed with some inherent structural redundancy. However, for the retro-fit project in particular, the available structural capacity of the roof may well limit the depth of substrate that can be used, thus constraining the choice of green roof system. An assessment of structural capacity is a prerequisite for any green roof project and should be carried out by a qualified structural engineer.

The structural capacity of an existing building can be increased for the purpose of retrofitting a green roof, but this is time consuming and expensive. In certain circumstances it may be possible to offset the mass of a green roof. For example, on an inverted warm roof this may be achieved by replacing the paving slabs (or other materials that provide ballast for the insulation layer) with the green roof system.

For a new building it is important that the green roof system is specified in some detail at the concept design stage. This either allows for any additional structural requirements to be accommodated within the building design or, for the green roof specification to be altered, to meet the structural requirements of the building design. A building in the course of being built can usually be altered to increase its structural capacity, but this is an expensive and time-consuming process and may delay the build.

There are many examples where the green roof system has not been considered in sufficient detail until late in the design stage or even during the construction stage; this has compromised the green roof design or even eliminated it altogether. It is unlikely that a client will be happy at building completion when they discover that their expected accessible intensive roof garden has become an inaccessible extensive roof.

Green roofs are normally designed not to exceed the minimum structural capacity across the whole of the roof area. However, a roof does not usually have a uniform structural capacity over its whole area. Greatest capacity is found over beams, columns and walls, whereas minimum capacity is normally found at points furthest away from these. This variation in structural capacity can be utilised to achieve a more radical green roof design. For example, a lightweight substrate at a depth of 50 mm may only be possible in certain areas, but a heavier weight substrate to a depth of 300 mm may be possible in areas where structural capacity is higher. This mix of substrate types and depths provides different growing conditions which encourages a wider variety of plant species (Brenniesen, 2003). The structural engineer should be consulted and should approve the proposed variations.

Figure 10.10 *Zurich railway station (courtesy S Wilson)*

The Zurich Railway Station canopy green roof makes use of greater structural capacity over the roof supporting columns to accommodate a greater substrate depth (Figure 10.10). This provides a variety of habitats that attract different plants, invertebrates and animals.

10.6 Fire resistance

Intensive green roofs have relatively deep soils that are regularly irrigated and so are resistant to fire. Extensive green roofs can easily be designed to provide adequate fire resistance by adopting the following precautions (FLL, 2002):

- the substrate should be at least 30 mm deep and contain a maximum of 20 per cent organic material
- the forms of vegetation constitute a low fire load (ie they provide a low volume of combustible matter that can act as a fuel to feed a fire)
- 0.5 m wide gravel fire breaks should be provided around openings, in front of walls or other structures that rise from the roof and around the edges of the roof (Figure 10.11).

For larger roofs gravel fire breaks should be provided at 40 m spacing.

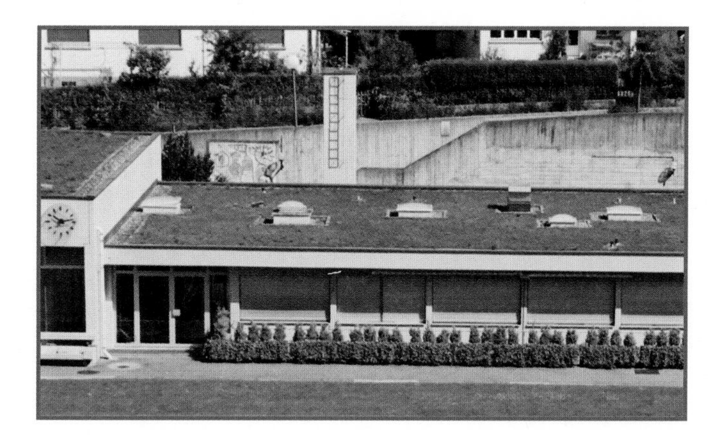

Figure 10.11 *Gravel fire breaks around upstands and walls (courtesy S Wilson)*

Introduction and background
Green roofs
Green walls
Nest boxes and other features
Appendices
Glossary, Abbreviations, References

Green roof design considerations: Key points

- where a green roof is being implemented to meet specific habitat or species objectives, the roof design and system used should be tailored to meet the specific circumstances of the site and local habitats
- a detailed assessment should be undertaken that considers: feasibility and constraints (eg structural limitations), substrate type, vegetation type and the possibilities for including additional landscape features (eg logs or boulders)
- the implementation of a successful biodiverse green roof requires a dynamic working relationship between ecologists, structural and civil engineers, landscape architects, horticulturalists, and green roof system suppliers
- green roofs provide interception storage and it is possible to allow for their attenuating effect in the design of a SUDS scheme
- the most common way of designing green roofs into SUDS schemes is to allow a reduced runoff coefficient when analysing single storm events
- the main factor that affects the water retention of green roofs is the storage capacity of the substrate and drainage layer
- green roofs will be most effective from a drainage point of view when they are combined with other SUDS technology to form a stormwater management train. This can have a significant impact in reducing the requirement for downstream storage
- the green roof peak rate of runoff can be less than or equal to the greenfield rate for rainfall depths up to three times the maximum water retention capacity of the substrate
- when designing a green roof careful consideration should be given to the limitations imposed by the slope of the roof. As the steepness of the slope increases, issues of slope stability and moisture retention arise. Typically intensive green roofs are constructed on slopes of up to 5 degrees and extensive roofs on slopes of up to 45 degrees
- in most cases the introduction of a green roof will have loading implications for the building. Any roof must be sufficiently engineered to carry the roof self-weight (including saturated green roof materials) and intermittent loads from wind, snow and human access. In the case of new build the green roof system should be specified at the concept design stage to allow any additional structural requirements to be accommodated in the building design (or conversely for the green roof design to be altered). **The impact of the green roof on the structure must be assessed by a structural engineer**
- on inverted roofs, the use of an extensive green roof system may have a negligible effect on the structural load as the green roof materials can replace the gravel or paving slabs that are used for ballast on this type of roof
- geen roofs can easily be designed to provide adequate fire resistance by using a minimum of 30 mm of substrate with a maximum of 20 per cent organic material. 0.5 m wide gravel fire breaks should be provided around openings, in front of structures that rise from the roof and around the edges of the roof. On larger roofs gravel fire breaks should be provided at 40 m spacing.

11 GREEN ROOF CONSTRUCTION, MAINTENANCE AND PERFORMANCE

11.1 Constructability

There is no point specifying a green roof that cannot be built due to access limitations or logistical problems. Consideration of how any material is to be procured, delivered, stored and installed is important. The bulkiest element of a green roof is the growing substrate. For a very simple green roof construction with a small area, it may well be practical to store the materials at ground level and to then lift the materials to the roof location manually or by using small-scale bucket lifts. However, for a larger scale project of, say, 1000 m² with a substrate depth of 150 mm, this is inappropriate. For this type of project, the only practical method is to use a crane or to pump the substrate to the roof level (some proprietary substrates cannot be pumped).

For larger scale projects, the contractor will address the majority of construction issues. However, it should be remembered that contractors will have to position necessary equipment around the perimeter of the building. This may affect the choice of construction method or phasing, depending on the availability of space around the building, or it may actually make certain green roof designs impractical as there is no suitable access to allow equipment to raise materials to the roof.

Storage of materials can also be critical. Elements such as waterproofing materials should be transported to site, stored and installed in a way that ensures that they are not damaged. One green roof installed in London saved £10 000 because temporary decking was not required over the roof to protect the waterproofing while other construction works took place.

Substrates are bulky and may require off-site storage. Complicated substrates may be made up of several different elements that need to be mixed correctly to create the desired final composition. Again, where this is to be carried out and how it is to be stored should be planned.

11.2 Quality

Quality issues for a green roof can be divided into reliability and biological function. For reliability the most commonly asked question is: "Does it leak?" The answer is no – not if a properly specified waterproofing system has been competently installed. Most extensive green roof systems are essentially a conventional flat roof construction with additional layers on top. If the conventional element of the roof is not constructed correctly from the appropriate materials, then it and the green roof may fail. However, if a green roof leaks, unlike a conventional roof, additional expense and time should be spent removing the substrate and other layers to find and mend the leak, and finally to reinstate the green roof.

It cannot be stressed enough that to ensure construction quality the appropriate materials should be specified and installed by competent contractors. The green roof should be considered as a system and not as a discrete component. Throughout the construction stage, appropriate testing of construction and installation quality should be carried out.

Any green roof design needs to consider the type of vegetation that will be grown and choose a compatible root barrier to prevent damage to the waterproof layer by aggressive root systems. The membrane manufacturer should be consulted on the most appropriate barrier to the type of membrane used. For warm roofs further consideration should be given to the effect of the green roof upon the long-term properties of the integral insulation layer. In particular, for inverted roofs the insulation should not degrade in the long-term when exposed to water.

The second element of quality relates to the biological function of the roof. Where the client wishes to create a certain type of habitat, due consideration should be given to the choice of substrate, plant type, planting method, microclimate, regional climate and post-installation plant care, to ensure that the client's aspirations are realised. It is not uncommon for a green roof to be correctly specified and constructed only for the plant species to fail due to poor post-installation care, usually as a result of under-watering and fertilising.

11.3 Health and safety

Health and safety is an important requirement of any project. Green roof projects involve working with heavy and bulky materials often at heights. Care and attention should be given to how specific tasks are to be carried out without anybody being placed in a position of danger. Compliance in the UK with the Health and Safety at Work Act 1974 will be essential. Particular attention should be paid to the prevention of falls from roofs, since they are the biggest single cause of death in the UK construction industry (Tables 11.1 and 11.2), and probably the major cause of death in the industry worldwide.

Table 11.1 *UK construction deaths (HSE, 1998)*

Cause	Number of deaths
Falls	214
Collapse or overturning	62
Struck by a vehicle	56
Struck by moving/flying object	37
Electrical	26
Other	37

Table 11.2 *UK construction deaths from falls (HSE, 1998)*

Type of fall	Number of deaths
Roofs	76
Ladder	44
Scaffold	43
Floor/surface	17
Steel	9
Other	25

All the activities to be carried out on a roof throughout its life should be considered at the design stage so that health and safety requirements can be accommodated. The Construction (Design and Management) Regulations 2007 (CDM) require that the design of any structure is undertaken so as to minimise the risks to those involved in its construction, operation and maintenance. This means that green roof designers need to ensure that, for example, the green roof materials can be safely placed without exposing workers to unacceptable risk. The key requirement of the CDM Regulations is that designers should identify hazards and then design them out wherever possible. If the hazards cannot reasonably be avoided they need to be reduced and then controlled.

With respect to the installation of green roof systems, potentially hazardous activities include:

- access to the roof (special care is required on small projects such as extensions, etc)
- working close to unprotected edges
- use of hazardous materials and hazardous operations (eg hot asphalt and bitumen)
- handling materials (heavy or awkward shapes)
- dropping items on to people below the roof.

Access to the roof will be needed for construction and to allow planned and reactive maintenance of not just the roof, but also of any electrical or mechanical services that may be associated with it. Permanent internal access is preferable as it is more reliable and less weather dependant. External access should be by fixed ladder or mobile work platforms. The least preferred method of access is by temporary ladder, which requires a minimum of two operatives for safe use, is slow to use, and may be difficult to position due to the roof design.

A permanent perimeter handrail or restraint system (Figure 11.1) may need to be installed or provision made for the installation of a temporary system. The method of working should prevent tools and debris from the roof falling on people below.

Figure 11.1 *A permanent restraint system for the installation and maintenance of the green roof of Roots and Shoots, Lambeth, London (courtesy P Early)*

Elements on the roof, such as roof lights should be robust and not present an undue tripping hazard. Any areas of the roof not safe for walking on should be permanently separated off with barriers.

11.4 Establishing the plant community

The majority of extensive green roofs, require little or no post-installation management, as they provide semi-natural, self-seeding habitats that are largely maintenance free. In contrast, for semi-intensive and intensive green roofs, it will be necessary in most cases to manage the establishment of plants, usually through irrigation, weeding and the application of fertiliser.

Client expectations will play a part in determining requirements for management to support the establishment of plant communities. For instance where the client expects particular plant communities to be established either for aesthetic reasons or to support biodiversity objectives, the roof is likely to require more intensive management. There might also be expectations from the client for the desired plant communities to be established within a certain time period. In such circumstances, either the client should be advised, in advance, to accept that the establishment of the plant community may take some time, or the green roof should be included in an earlier phase of the building construction to allow the plant communities to establish themselves within the desired timescales. It is possible that mature plant communities, eg sedum mats, can be introduced at the outset having the effect of producing an instant green roof plant community, perhaps with a local seed mix to enable greater diversity in the long-term.

The time of year is also an important factor in the establishment of vegetation, as environmental factors such as rainfall, temperature and light will influence the growth of the desired plant species. The client should be aware of the impact of such factors on the establishment of the plant communities, allowing either expectations to be reduced or the construction programme to be tailored to provide the greatest chance of the expectations being met.

11.5 Maintenance

The amount of maintenance required is dependent on the type of green roof constructed, the specific system used, the environmental conditions to which it is subject, and client expectations. It is important that maintenance is considered at the roof concept stage and, either a budget and resource allocated, or the green roof redesigned to reduce maintenance.

Intensive and simple intensive green roofs require relatively high levels of maintenance, with similar levels of irrigation, weeding and general maintenance as is associated with similar landscapes at ground level. Extensive green roofs on the other hand are normally designed to require a low level of maintenance, perhaps no more than an annual inspection. However, even for extensive green roofs there will be variations depending on the type of system used. Sedum based extensive green roof systems may need maintenance to prevent the desired species being out competed by other plants. In contrast, naturally seeded green roofs, such as those found in Switzerland, are generally seeded with a local flower mix and require little or no maintenance as they develop into self maintaining systems.

Levels of maintenance will increase as green roof design moves away from the natural and becomes more aesthetically driven. Normally a green roof will require more maintenance in the first few years to encourage establishment of plant species. It is common in the UK for there to be a period of irrigation and application of fertiliser in the early stages, as there is a client expectation that the roof be vegetated as quickly as possible. In addition, there can be unnecessary client-driven maintenance to weed green roofs due to prejudice or ignorance of plant species and their place on green roofs.

Environmental factors such as rainfall, temperature and light will influence the need for maintenance (eg irrigation), but such maintenance requirements can be reduced by selecting species suited to the particular environment.

It may be undesirable and unsustainable to design a roof that requires irrigation. Extensive roofs are generally designed to reflect the seasons and therefore regular irrigation is not generally required beyond the early establishment of the vegetation.

Where irrigation is required it is preferable to use stored rainfall or reclaimed greywater for these purposes (see Section 7.4). The timing and volume of irrigation water used may be controlled by software linked to a weather station that can help reduce wastage.

11.6 Costs

The capital cost of a green roof is generally greater than that for a conventional roof. However, the whole life cost of a building with a green roof may be less than if the roof was of conventional design, once the reduced costs of cooling and heating and the lifespan of waterproofing is taken into account. So it is important to consider both capital and operational costs of green roofs.

The additional capital cost of a green roof compared to a conventional roofing system will depend on the following factors:

- **type of roof (ie beneath the green roof)** – generally a green roof is an additional cost. However, as discussed in Section 10.5, on an inverted roof it may be possible to replace the paving slabs or other materials that provide ballast for the insulation with the green roof system, as long as the weight requirements are fulfilled. In these circumstances some of the costs of the shingle and paving slabs are removed. A review of roofs in London showed that a number of green roofs on inverted systems only cost between 17 and 25 per cent more than a conventional roof (Frith and Gedge, 2004)
- **type of green roof system** – intensive and simple intensive green roof systems tend to be more expensive as they require greater structural capacity within the building, a greater volume of substrate, greater variety of plants and higher levels of maintenance. Extensive green roofs, although less expensive, will vary in price depending on the type of system used. In general pre-grown systems are the most expensive (eg sedum mat), and systems that use locally sourced aggregate and are seeded or utilise natural colonisation are the cheapest
- **height of the building** – this will impact on the construction costs associated with raising the materials and other elements required to roof level
- **size of the roof** – in general there is an economy of scale with green roofs; the larger the green roof area the less the cost per m^2
- **number of intrusions and interfering factors** – elements within the building design such as skylights, industrial plant, safety rails and wires can lead to increased costs because of the need to provide details to protect such elements
- **initial maintenance and irrigation** – all green roof systems need initial maintenance and irrigation to help establish the vegetation. Typically for all systems the soil should be kept moist for the initial four weeks to all the plants to establish root growth. The level of maintenance and irrigation after this brief initial period and the associated costs will vary depending on the type of system used. Extensive roofs require the least maintenance
- **programme** – generally, the earlier in the design and construction process the decision to incorporate a green roof is made, the cheaper it will be to install. Decisions taken after the design brief has been set will likely require costly design revisions and delays to the build
- **repairs** – if waterproofing does leak green roofs can be more difficult to repair than a standard roof. The removal of vegetation and substrate layers, repair of leaks and then re-establishment of the green roof can be costly. Costs can be reduced by using modular green roof systems, where the green roof is established in separate modules or blocks. This type of system enables discrete areas of the roof to be removed. A number of leak detection systems are available which can be buried within the green roof system.

If the roof is installed and maintained correctly, the risk of leaks should be no higher than for a conventional roof, and may in fact be lower as a result of the additional protection the green roof provides to the waterproofing layer. Moisture mats and root barriers should be used to protect the waterproofing material.

11.7 Assessment and monitoring

The success of a green roof should be measured against the original design criteria. A site specific monitoring regime will be required if a formal assessment of the success of a scheme is required.

Specific considerations may include:

- Has it achieved the original design intention?
- Has it helped to meet any legislative requirements, BAP targets or planning conditions?
- Is it being maintained to the required standard?
- Are there any health and safety problems?
- Is it meeting stormwater management standards?
- Is it meeting thermal performance targets?
- Is it enjoyed by people?

The nature of the monitoring regime will depend on the indicators against which performance is being measured. Some examples are given below:

- stormwater management targets – it is likely that automatic equipment will be required to monitor levels of rainfall runoff (this can be expensive)
- biodiversity targets –this will require a programme of surveys to be undertaken by an ecologist
- maintenance targets – monitored by regular site inspections.

Green roof construction, maintenance and performance: Key points

- consideration should be given to how access limitations and logistics will affect the delivery and installation of green roof materials, especially substrates, which are the bulkiest element of a green roof
- on smaller roofs substrate can be lifted manually or by using small bucket lifts. However, for larger projects the most practical method is to use a crane or to pump the substrate to the roof level
- ensuring the health and safety of workers and the public is an important requirement of any project. Green roof projects involve working with heavy and bulky materials often at heights, so particular attention should be paid to the prevention of falls from roofs
- a perimeter handrail or restraint system will be required for people who construct or maintain the roof
- the time of year is an important factor in the establishment of vegetation, as environmental factors such as rainfall, temperature and light will influence the growth of the desired plant species. This will affect the programme time for the roof to establish and the aesthetics of the roof in the first year after completion
- intensive roofs require the most maintenance. Extensive roofs require the least. Naturally seeded green roofs require little or no maintenance as they develop into self maintaining systems
- the capital cost of a green roof is generally greater than for a conventional roof. However, the whole life cost of a building with a green roof may be less than if the roof was of conventional design, once the cost of cooling and heating and the lifespan of waterproofing is taken into account. Once a green roof is integrated into a drainage design it should not be removed without checking the capacity of the underground drainage system (which may need increasing)
- the additional capital cost of a green roof compared to a conventional roofing system is dependent on a number of factors including:
    - on an inverted roof system the green roof can replace the cost of shingle or paving slabs
    - systems that use locally sourced aggregate and are naturally seeded are the cheapest
    - the building height will affect the cost of raising the materials and other elements required to roof level
    - there is an economy of scale with green roofs
    - elements such as skylights, industrial plant, safety rails and wires can increase costs because of the need to provide details to protect such elements
- the success of a green roof should be measured against the original design criteria. A site specific monitoring regime will be required if a formal assessment of the success of a scheme is required.

C Green walls

Quai Brankley, Paris (courtesy G Grant)

12 INTRODUCTION TO GREEN WALLS AND THEIR BENEFITS

12.1 Introduction

Walls that have plants growing on, or integrated within them are called green or living walls. Green walls provide a living and self-regenerating cladding system, using plants that can be grown on and planted into vertical surfaces. The process of greening a wall is called "façade greening".

Figure 12.1 *A deciduous green wall providing an otherwise featureless wall with visual interest and greater habitat value even in mid-winter, Aston University, Birmingham, January/June 2006 (courtesy P Early)*

Figure 12.2 *The combined green walls and green roofs of Brunel Street car park, Birmingham, provide habitat and aesthetic benefit along the city centre ring road (courtesy P Early)*

12.2 Historical perspective

Climbing plants have been cultivated on buildings since antiquity. In the Ancient Greek and Roman empires grapevines and olive and nut trees were purposefully trained on the walls of buildings. This is a tradition that has largely fallen out of use in the UK, but has continued to the present day particularly in Central Europe (Figure 12.3).

From the 16th century onwards non-European species of climbing plants were introduced, and the formal gardening fashion of the seventeenth and eighteenth centuries included the greening of walls with plants such as clematis *Clematis spp.* and climbing rose *Rosa spp.*. South facing "warm" walls were also used to grow fruits such as apricot *Prunus spp.*, peach *Prunus spp.* and pear *Pyrus spp.*.

Figure 12.3
Grape vines growing on the walls of an old inn, northern France (courtesy P Early)

Green walls continued to find favour during the late eighteenth and early nineteenth centuries as an element in the major romantic gardens of the time, often as an integral part of ruins or follies.

The use of the green wall as a modern architectural element began in Europe. While climbers had been used traditionally on buildings for centuries, modern methods, including the use of high-tensile steel cables and other support structures enabled the concept to be used more adventurously. With suitable species selection heights of up to 25 m can be attained; alternatively plants can be grown in large irrigated containers suspended from the wall itself, enabling even greater heights to be reached.

Large-scale green wall systems are still a relatively new concept. A solid research base has developed in Europe, and in particular Germany, over the last 20 years. Experiments to determine the environmental performance of green walls have been carried out, and regulations and specifications published. Continuing active research is a major concern for several German academic institutions. There is also growing interest in North America where a number of products are under development.

During the same period a professional green wall industry has emerged, providing advice on plant selection, plant supply, the installation of support structures on the building fabric, and maintenance. The green wall industries of Germany, Switzerland and Austria are now world-leaders in this field. There is at present, however, a limited amount of information available in the public domain on the subject.

12.3 Types of green wall

Green walls generally fall into one of the following three broad categories:

1. Walls with climbing plants, either supported by the wall itself, a structure attached to the wall or a self-standing structure.
2. Hanging walls, which allow plants to hang down from planters suspended from a height.
3. Walls with plants growing within them, either purposefully or accidentally.

All of these techniques can be used to great effect to improve the urban environment and a brief description of these techniques is provided below. The remaining sections of Part C will focus primarily on the use of climbing plants.

12.3.1 Walls with climbing plants

Climbing plants can be used for to create green walls in the following ways:

- supported by a wall – self-supporting climbers
- supported by a structure on a wall (eg a trellis) – twining and other climbers
- supported by a self-standing structure away from a wall (eg a pergola).

Further detail on the use of climbing plants is provided in Section 12.4.1.

12.3.2 Hanging walls

Hanging walls use plants that are allowed to drape over a parapet (Figure 12.4) or from a trough (Figure 12.5) and down a wall. The advantage of this is that no additional support is required and hence the plants do not have to come into contact with the wall. The plants require appropriate soil and moisture retention conditions and sufficient anchoring to prevent them from blowing off the roof due to high winds. Many of the species of climbing plants are also suitable for use in hanging walls. Hanging walls can be an attractive solution to greening the top of high walls and as an alternative to growing a conventional ground based green wall.

Figure 12.4 *A parapet hanging wall purposely integrated onto a building, Evergreen House, Euston, London (courtesy P Early)*

Figure 12.5 *A façade mounted trough based hanging wall, Cotton Centre, London Bridge, London (courtesy P Early)*

12.3.3 Walls with plants growing within them

Ever since walls have been constructed plants have grown on and within them. Dry stone walls in particular have provided ideal habitat for a variety of species that have found suitable habitat within the interstices of the wall itself. Plants like wall pennywort *Umbilicus rupstris*, wall rue *Asplenium ruta-muraria* and wall flower *Erysimum cheiri* attest to the special habitat conditions that such walls can provide for a wide variety of plants.

Even mortared walls can provide sanctuary for certain species – butterfly bush *Buddleja davidii* being an example of a vigorous shrub that utilises the alkaline conditions created by mortar to gain a foothold on walls at all heights, especially in towns and cities where it can cause concern among structural engineers. Mosses and lichens need very little material in order for them to take hold, and old walls in particular have provided botanists with rich habitat to study such specialist plants. A common species is *Tortula muralis*, the wall screw moss.

Now designers and ecologists are taking this one step further by deliberately creating walls as habitats for plants and animals. Green walls created out of a framework of fast growing willow and packed with soil in which a variety of plants, including grasses, can grow, are often used in a variety of construction or civil engineering schemes.

More radical still is the creation of a structure attached to the wall into which a variety of species can be planted. The wall includes an irrigation system that provides the plants with water and nutrients to ensure that they remain fresh and alive (Figures 12.6 and 12.7 and the photo of a building on Quai Branley, Paris at the start of this section). The visual impact of such walls is dramatic to say the least, but they also provide a living vertical habitat with their own intrinsic biodiversity value providing a special environment in which other plants and animals can gain shelter (refer to Case study 15).

Figure 12.6 *Plug planted green wall, Paradise Park Children's Centre, London, a few months after construction and planting (courtesy P Early)*

Figure 12.7

A detail of the plug planted green wall showing the construction and variety of plants used (courtesy P Early)

12.4 Benefits of green walls

Walls occupy a far greater surface area of buildings than roofs. They are sometimes blank, featureless, unattractive and often devoid of habitat value. Using plants to green walls introduces colour, variety and provides benefits in terms of amenity, biodiversity, thermal efficiency and amelioration of pollutants, all for a very small ground level footprint. The creation of foraging and nesting habitat through the use of green walls can also complement the use of green roofs and nest boxes.

12.4.1 Benefits for biodiversity

In areas of limited potential for traditional forms of greenery (eg parks, gardens etc) the use of green walls can offer an elegant, practical and cost effective solution to help to meet a number of regional and local biodiversity action plan targets.

The advantages of green walls for biodiversity are potentially very great. Any climbing plant provides habitat for invertebrates, such as insects and spiders, which in turn will be food for insect-eating birds and bats. Any climber will also act as a transit route for wildlife between habitat at ground level and that established on green roofs. Green walls make use of vertical space that would otherwise be lifeless; they can provide considerable area of habitat while only occupying a small amount of ground area.

The choice of climbing plant species will affect the biodiversity interest of the wall. For example, ivy *Hedera helix* is excellent, because of its branching structure which offers plenty of places for birds to nest and roost. It is late flowering so it provides an important seasonal nectar source for insects, and as an evergreen it provides good habitat for hibernating insects, and winter roosting for birds (Figure 12.8). Bats have also been found roosting behind dense ivy cover. Kiwi fruit *Actinidia chinensis* is not evergreen, but its branching structure makes it useful for birds. In contrast, Boston ivy *Parthenocissus tricuspidata*, has a very tight wall-hugging profile and is deciduous, and as a consequence is not so valuable in this respect.

Early flowering species are similarly important as insects such as butterflies and moths emerging from hibernation. The presence of this rich invertebrate prey makes green walls attractive to feeding bats.

Figure 12.8 *A bird's nest located within an ivy green wall (courtesy P Early)*

Most flowering species will offer a nectar source for insects, and a range of species can be chosen in order to cover the key April to October period. Fruiting species offer a food source for birds during the autumn period. Ivy berries in particular are a good winter food source.

Nesting and roosting opportunities for birds and bats can be maximised by the use of appropriate boxes (see Part D), which would be particularly beneficial in the first few years after installation while the climbing plants are still being established. Locating potential roosting and nesting sites in climbers offers a clear advantage for urban wildlife, as the sites are inaccessible to cats, the main predator of urban bird life.

Green walls are specifically referred to in a number of urban and built up areas' action plans. The Camden biodiversity action plan mentions the use of green walls to *"...Promote the use of artificial habitats eg ... the greening of vertical surfaces, in areas where "natural" habitat is lacking."* Certainly species such as house sparrow *Passer domesticus*, which is a BAP species in a number of places in the UK, are likely to benefit from dense climbers which provide nesting and feeding opportunities. Importantly, they provide the dense cover this species needs to "socialise". Several other uncommon and declining species, including the UK BAP species song thrush *Turdus philomelos* and spotted flycatcher *Musciapa striata*, nest in climbers.

The importance of climbers and other green wall types for common species should not be overlooked. These include blackbird *Turdus merula*, robin *Erithacus rubecula*, mistle thrush *Turdus viscivorus*, wren *Troglodytes troglodytes*, dunnock *Prunella modularis* and the common finch species (BTO, 2005). Climbers are also known to be used for winter roosting by species such as pied wagtail *Motacilla alba*. A small wall in Leicestershire was observed to hold a roost of over 150 individual pied wagtails in early January 2000, and climbers on Lewisham Town Hall hold a roost of over 200 birds.

Figure 12.9 *Green wall, London, where a pair of blackbirds nest (courtesy Peabody Trust)*

12.4.2 Benefits for climate change mitigation and adaptation

In the summer, climbers can significantly reduce the maximum local external temperatures of a building by shading walls from the sun; the daily temperature fluctuation being reduced by as much as 50 per cent. The effectiveness of this cooling is related primarily to the total area shaded and evapotranspiration, rather than the thickness of the climber (Köhler, 1993). Together with the insulation effect, diurnal temperature fluctuations at the wall surface can be reduced from between 10°C and 60°C to between 5°C and 30°C (Peck *et al*, 1999).

The use of climbers to reduce building solar overheating is most effective if they are used on south facing walls that are in the sun for most of the day, and on west facing walls that experience afternoon heating.

Green walls can be used not only to shade walls, but if designed correctly can contribute to shading windows and other glazed areas, thereby reducing the air conditioning cooling load and making the internal environment more comfortable (as the building occupants no longer receive the same amount of direct solar radiation). The use of green walls in this manner is called "bioshading" (Case study 12). Bioshading may make the internal building space less prone to sunlight glare. However, diffuse light levels may be lower, which could result in a requirement for additional artificial lighting. An appropriate balance needs to be achieved.

In the winter, evergreen climbers can provide insulation by maintaining a layer of still air between the plant and the wall, which reduces convection at the wall surface. Reducing convection by 75 per cent can reduce heating demand by 25 per cent (Peck *et al*, 1999) although the results rely on a number of factors including wall insulation and thickness. Heat loss through convection is reduced to some extent by the interwoven stems of deciduous climbers during winter. Overall, the effectiveness of winter insulation provided by climbing plants is related to the thickness and coverage of growth, which is generally related to the age of the plant. In some cases, however, growth patterns change as the plant ages, eg there may be a reduction in the dense twiggy growth that forms the most effective insulation.

The reduction of wall wetting, on certain types of walling, can lessen the amount of cooling through evaporation at the wall's surface, which would otherwise result in energy loss through the building fabric.

Figure 12.10 ***Green wall providing protection for the walls from driving snow (courtesy P Early)***

Evapotranspiration and shading provided by a green wall can result in a more comfortable microclimate adjacent to the building. The natural plant processes can use large quantities of water, which makes green walls a potential SUDS component.

Reduction of solar heating on the sides of buildings helps to reduce the "urban heat island effect" discussed in Section 8.4. The green wall reduces this effect by intercepting both light and heat radiation; the plants either reflect a high proportion of the solar radiation received or use it to drive internal processes such as transpiration. This solar radiation would otherwise be largely absorbed and converted to heat by the building surfaces.

Case study 13 University of Brighton, green wall research project, Brighton, UK

Bioshading experiment at the University of Brighton (courtesy M Lam)

Location	School of the Environment, University of Brighton
Type of development	Research has been carried out into Bioshading, that is, the thermal shading effect of climbing plants.
Planting	Virginia Creeper
Researchers	Marta Hoi Yan Lam, Kenneth Ip, Andrew Miller
Comments	Specific research was carried out to understand the thermal shading performance of a deciduous plant canopy for use in preventing excessive solar radiation overheating in buildings. The bioshader was located on the outside face of an office with the identical office next door used as a control (similar occupancy, but without a bioshade). The bioshader consisted of Virginia creepers trained on a metal framework for support. Measurements were made for internal and external solar flux, external relative humidity and air temperature. Internal air velocity, relative humidity and air temperature were measured in the ducts of the controlled mechanical room ventilation plant. Results of analysis showed solar transmittances of between 0.43 and 0.14 for one to five leaf layers respectively and an overall maximum shading coefficient of 0.55 during the growing season. The shading coefficient was near zero between mid November and late April, when there were no leaves on the plant, thereby allowing full winter sunlight into the building. Hence, a substantial reduction of solar radiation was observed during the period when solar radiation overheating of buildings occurs, but without being detrimental to the reception of winter sunlight. In practical terms the results indicate a reduction in room temperature of 4–6°C compared to the control during peak summer external temperatures. There is a constant higher relative humidity in the test room than that of the control room. Information provided by Marta Hoi Yan Lam, Kenneth Ip and Andrew Miller, School of Environment, University of Brighton.

Case study 14 Humbolt University, Berlin, Germany

(Left) Institute for Physic, Adleshof. Photo taken during the winter when vegetation is at its minimum (courtesy P Early). (Right) An example of the vegetation growth in the summer on two courtyard facades (courtesy M Schmidt)

Location	Institute for Physics, Humbolt University, Berlin-Adleshof, Germany
Type of development	Experimental green walls to investigate the potential of green walls to reduce energy consumption through shading and evapotranspiration. Also considered sustainable drainage systems, passive cooling, adiabatic cooling and rain water recycling for green wall irrigation.
Type of green wall	The building has been built with 150 sealed troughs mounted on four floors on all nine building façades.
Architects	Augustin and Frank, Berlin
Landscape architect	Landscape architect; Buero Berger and Tischer, Berlin
Green wall designer	Marco Schmidt, Technical University, Berlin Prof Dr Manfred Koehler, University of Neubrandenburg PD Dr Wernicke, Humbolt University, Berlin
Building cost	€96 million

continued

Case study 14 Humbolt University, Berlin, Germany (contd)

Comments	Separate irrigation systems ensure that the water level in each trough is maintained at a constant level (rainwater is used for irrigation where possible). 120 sensors constantly monitor the green wall and measure parameters such as solar isolation, rainwater, irrigation water, temperature, humidity, wind speed etc. Evapotranspiration is derived from the measurement of the metered water supply and from this the evaporative cooling can be quantified. There are also experiments in plant behaviour, such as using insulated and non-insulated troughs to determine the effect of winter temperatures upon the growth of plant root systems (insulated troughs record a minimum soil temperature of 0°C, for non-insulated troughs the minimum recorded temperature is -10°C). Continuous monitoring at the site began in 2004 and preliminary findings on the south facing façade indicate that the mean evapotranspiration rate in the summer (between July and August) is between 3–4 mm per day (depending on which floor the trough is located). This rate of evapotranspiration represents 157 kWh per day of solar radiation used for cooling. The experimental data from this study and other projects has already been used in conjunction with historical five minute precipitation data of the past twenty to thirty years to provide long-term simulations and predictions of precipitation and potential and actual evapotranspiration. This is an important step in allowing the translation of real measurements to different climatic conditions and to determine the potential for stormwater management and passive cooling using green walls.
Completion date	2002

12.4.3 Aesthetic benefits

The greening of walls can, in a similar way to the planting of trees, do much to improve public enjoyment of the urban environment. Large climbers, up to 25 m high, can be visually dramatic, as well as softening hard surfaces. Climbing plants have traditionally been seen as "add-ons" to buildings, but the new approach, being pioneered in Switzerland and Germany, is to see them as integral to the urban design concept. In addition to being used on buildings, climbers can be used on freestanding structures such as giant "pergolas" or on poles. (Figure 12.11)

Figure 12.11 *An example of a pergola. The Rose Garden, Hyde Park, London (courtesy P Early)*

12.4.4 Other benefits

Contrary to received wisdom, climbers on buildings can actually help to protect the surface of the building from damage. Climbers can defend the wall from very heavy driving rainfall and hail, and may also protect modern cladding systems from damage caused by ultra-violet light. Green walls also reduce both the incidence and consequence of the splash back of rain at the foot of a building wall, a phenomenon that can compromise the building's damp course layer in extreme circumstances.

Climbers have been shown to be highly effective at trapping dust and concentrating certain dust-derived pollutants in their tissues, particularly in those that are then discarded. In a study of Boston ivy *Parthenocissus tricuspidata*, lead and cadmium concentrations have been shown to be highest in dead leaves and wood. These heavy metals are taken out of the atmosphere and rain, and concentrated in a form that then falls to the ground (Köhler, 1993). If dead leaves and branches are removed and disposed of correctly, green walls can play a role in reducing the environmental hazards presented by these elements.

Plants absorb and breakdown a variety of pollutants, notably volatile organic compounds, and un-burnt hydrocarbons from vehicle exhaust. It is a reasonable assumption that urban climbers could play a role in reducing these in city areas.

Some research has been carried out into the precipitation of particulates on the leaves of green wall plants such as ivy alongside motorways in Germany (Köhler, 1993). The percentage of particulate coverage on the leaf surface was measured and it was found that particulates and dust covered 40 per cent of leaf surface with the leaf veins having up to 100 per cent coverage. The extent of coverage was about 4–6 g/m^2, depending upon vegetation density, with the more dense areas having the greater particulate coverage. A relationship was found between particulate distribution and height, with a reduction of particulate density the higher the vegetation was above ground level. Particulates and dust on the leaves bind to the leaf surfaces, and are composted along with the leaf when it falls from the plant.

This removal of particulates and dust from the urban environment by plants is an important function of a green wall. While no direct evidence of health studies for green wall particulate removal are in the public domain, it is well established that particulates and dust can cause health problems particularly for those with asthma and other respiratory conditions.

A few high profile green walls have been constructed for the purpose of improving urban outdoor air quality, such as the *Bio-lung* that was exhibited at the 2005 Expo in Japan (Japan Association for the 2005 World Exposition, 2005). A similar project is planned for the MFO Park, Basel, Switzerland, where a multi-story pergola structure is to be built with climbing plants growing throughout.

13 GREEN WALL DESIGN AND MAINTENANCE CONSIDERATIONS

As with green roofs, the benefits of installing a green wall will be maximised if it is planned from the outset of the building project. Design should include careful consideration of construction and maintenance issues to ensure success. Plants or structures coming away from a wall due to poor design and maintenance are neither attractive nor safe. Plants need management to get them to behave as the designer envisaged and will need removal, and possibly replacement if they fail. Careful consideration of aspect and microclimate will also be crucial to the success of a green wall, with direct sun or complete shade possible.

13.1 Standards and Regulations

There are no specific standards in the UK for the implementation of green walls, although any structure used to support a green wall should meet building regulations and gain planning consent. There are few international standards published. The most relevant international standard is that published by the German FLL organisation. Their standard; *Regulations for the Planning, Construction and Maintenance of Façade Greening with Climbing Plants*, was first published in 1995 and updated in 2000 (FLL, 2000) and identify the following potential benefits of green walls:

Aesthetics benefits

- visual improvement of the urban landscape
- increased opportunity to see plants and animals
- development of green areas in accordance with the aspirations of planners
- creation of locally distinct, identifiable urban areas through different types of greening
- part-compensation for the loss of green space through development.

Physical and climatic

- reduction of the physical and chemical wear of walls by reducing temperature extremes and UV
- protection of wall from wind and driving rain
- improved insulation against noise
- improved thermal insulation
- improved microclimate through regulating temperature extremes (evapotranspiration etc)
- reduction of surface radiation reflection to surrounding area (canyon radiative effect)
- impacts on local air humidity
- reduction of dust and particulates (through sedimentation onto plant surfaces)
- increase of pervious area to allow infiltration of rainwater
- energy savings in terms of heating and cooling.

The regulations identify the following issues that should be considered during the design and specification of a green wall:

Feasibility

- Given the location and context of the development is a green wall feasible? And, will it survive?
- What type of green wall is needed and appropriate?
- Will it add aesthetically to the development?
- What are the maintenance implications?

Design

- Will a framework be needed to support climbing plants – if so how will it be constructed and what materials will be used?
- Will a series of balconies, planters or other structures that support a variety of plant life be required?
- Is a special texture required for the facade that will enable plants to get a foothold?
- What plant species are best suited to the environment (aspect, drainage etc)?
- How much land will be required at the base of the wall to provide sufficient root space for climbing plants or to act as a foundation for any frameworks?
- What are the irrigation and other maintenance requirements?

Operational

- What are the maintenance requirements (pruning/weeding/irrigation)?
- How will you ensure the structural integrity of any framework?

13.2 Species selection

The specification of appropriate species for a green wall is the key to success. Critical issues that need to be considered include:

size – it is important that species are chosen that will not exceed the load capacity of the building façade or supports, and that will produce the required coverage

aspect – each aspect of a building provides a different microclimate and all aspects of urban sites should be considered on an individual basis as wind, rain and sun shading will differ considerably due to surrounding buildings. There are many commercially available plants that can suit a particular aspect. Consideration of aspect allows interesting plant combinations to be used throughout the building perimeter (RHS, 2001):

- *north-facing walls* receive little direct sunlight and provide a good environment for shade-loving climbing plants such as: ivies, virginia creeper group *Parthenocissus spp.* and climbing hydrangea group *Hydrangea spp.* and *Schizophragma spp.*. The temperature of a north-facing wall increases slowly throughout the day and so does not cause damage to plants
- *east-facing walls* receive several hours of direct sunlight in the morning and so climbing plants used on these walls do not need to be shade-loving. Care should be

taken with plant selection as, during winter and spring, the rapid warming of frozen leaves and buds in the early morning sunlight can cause plant damage

  - *south-facing walls* are subject to the maximum amount of sunlight. A proportion of the solar energy is stored in the wall even in winter, which warms the wall and provides several degrees of frost protection. This additional frost protection helps the survival of a number of otherwise marginal plants and encourages other plants to grow more vigorously
  - *west-facing walls* receive the direct afternoon and evening sunlight, and suit plants that require sunlight, but that do not thrive in long periods of intense, direct sunlight
  - plants on south and west-facing walls warm relatively slowly in comparison with an east facing wall and so are less prone to damage in winter and spring
  - both east and north facing walls can suffer from rain shadow and it may be necessary to position the plants away from the base of the wall to ensure they receive sufficient rainfall.

- **climbing mechanism** – as discussed in Section 12.3 some climbing plants may require support structures other than the wall itself. Equally, it may be necessary to provide a support structure if the plant species is incompatible with the building façade material. Consequently, the ability to provide support structures (eg space constraints) may impact on the choice of plant species
- **hanging mechanism** – where plants hang from a height down the wall this will effect species selection for example, to ensure plants can cope with the physical growing conditions
- **visual aspects** – visual appearance may or may not be regarded as important. Foliage quality is generally regarded as the most important characteristic. Where all year round foliage is desired, the choice of evergreens is limited
- **biodiversity aspects** – species vary considerably in the quantity and quality of the roosting space and food sources they provide. A variety of species may be grown together to increase the variety of food and roosting spaces available throughout the seasons
- **maintenance issues** – species vary in the amount of maintenance needed. The safety of persons around the wall and the integrity of the façade surface take priority
- **deciduous or evergreen** – there may be a preference for plants that shed leaves in the winter so that the wall surface can receive winter sunlight. Bioshading may be an important consideration for large glazed areas that are subject to solar overheating.

13.3 The use of climbing plants

There are many species of climbing plant that potentially can be used. They generally fall into one of the following two categories:

- self-supporting climbers
- twining climbers.

Further information on both these categories of climbing plants, as well as information on supports and fixings and root space requirements is provided in Sections 12.3.1 to 12.3.4.

13.3.1 Self-supporting climbers

Using either tiny roots that exploit the rough surfaces, minute cracks and interstices of building materials, or naturally adhesive tendrils, these species attach themselves to the wall surfaces (eg render, concrete and brick). They are normally not suitable for smooth cladding surfaces such as polished granite, marble, metal or even some concrete claddings, as they find insufficient anchorage. They do not necessarily need support mechanisms (although the plants will utilise these if they are present) and so they are very cheap to install. On certain wall surfaces, especially those made from soft materials, that have a paint finish, or that have lots of voids into which roots can creep, these types of plant may cause damage to the finish or the structure.

The following examples of self-supporting species grow vigorously and cause little or no damage to traditional stone or brick building surfaces.

Ivy *Hedera helix* is a native species, growing 10–20 m high, offering the widest range of biodiversity advantages. The fact that it is very robust, adaptable to all aspects, and self-supporting means that it is very versatile. Large-leaved introduced species, such as *H. canariensis*, offer a more decorative alternative. A disadvantage of ivy is that as it matures it develops shrubby growth that can project out from the building. This can be kept cut back as part of an annual maintenance programme.

Figure 13.1 *Overhanging ivy requiring maintenance. Not only is the plant becoming bushy and placing an increasing load on the supporting wall, it is also compromising the roof and covering windows (courtesy P Early)*

Figure 13.2 *An example of uncontrolled ivy growth causing structural problems (courtesy P Early)*

Figure 13.3 *Specialised ivy roots allow the plant to cling to wooden fencing (courtesy P Early)*

Virginia creeper *Parthenocissus quinquefolia* and Boston ivy *Parthenocissus tricuspidata* are popular climbers that utilise a sticky compound to adhere themselves to surfaces and grow to 20 m high. They are tolerant of a wide range of aspects, require minimal maintenance and are highly decorative particularly in the autumn.

Other self-supporting species include climbing hydrangea *Hydrangea petiolaris* and the climbing varieties of *Eunonymus fortunei*.

Figure 13.4 *Adhesive tendrils provide this plant with its support on a modern brick surface (courtesy P Early)*

Figure 13.5 shows that damage from climbing plants on the surface of buildings can be undetectable even after many years of plant growth, provided a suitable, durable climbing surface is used. Despite the ivy being removed some years previously, the roots remain attached to the wall. Roots and tendrils will be left behind on the wall surface and these may be difficult to remove and will remain for many years.

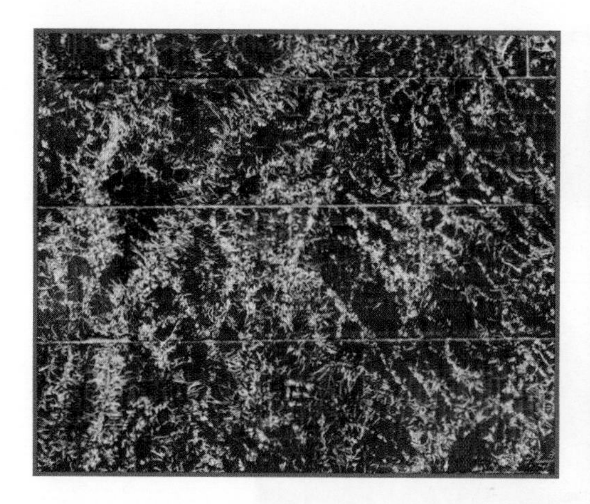

Figure 13.5 *Minimal wall damage from ivy growth (courtesy P Early)*

13.3.2 Twining climbers

These species extend shoots, which twist around structures that provide the plant with support. Typical supports include cables, wooden or metal trellis, pergolas etc. Different types of climber require different support systems – the visual appearance of which is a major factor in selection. Vertical cables have the least visual impact of any support system.

Species of twining climber include:

- Russian vine *Fallopia baldschuanica*. Extremely fast growing up to 30 m. Provides good thick growth that is attractive to nesting birds.
- Chinese wisteria *Wisteria sinensis* to 25 m high. Best for light aspects. Needs tensioned vertical cable for support. Spectacular in flower. Medium biodiversity value. Needs careful placing owing to vigour and thickness of lower stems with age. Low maintenance if properly sited, high if not.
- Ornamental vine, *Vitis coignetiae*. Tendril-climber, to 20 m high. Best with some sun. Quality foliage, spectacular in autumn. Needs to have trellis or both vertical and horizontal supports. Medium biodiversity value. Medium maintenance.
- Chocolate vine *Akebia quinata*. Twining climber to 10 m high. Light shade or sun. Good foliage and a dense pattern of growth, needing vertical supports or trellis. Medium biodiversity value. Medium maintenance.
- Hop *Humulus lupulus*. Twining climber to 7 m. Sun. Vigorous and attractive but as it dies back in winter this can be seen as “untidy” and so a disadvantage. High biodiversity value.
- Honeysuckles *Lonicera spp.*. Up to 7 m high. Useful for nectar and seed.
- Kiwi fruit *Actinidia chinensis*. Twining climber up to 12 m.
- Potato vine *Solanum jasminoides*. Scrambling climber growing up to 6 m.

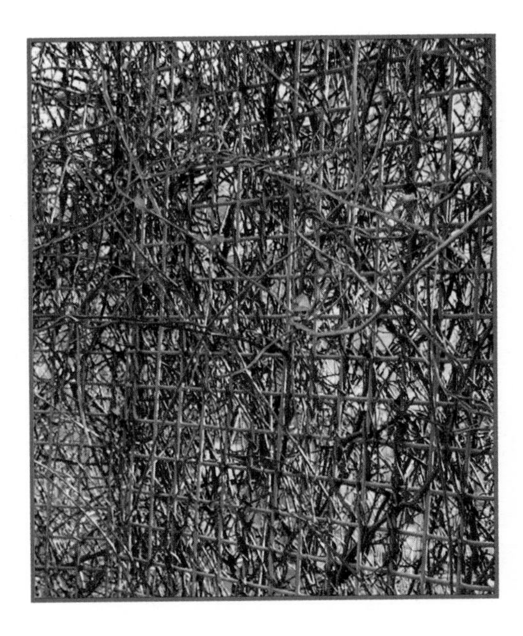

Figure 13.6

An example of a deciduous twining climber requiring support (courtesy P Early)

Mixing species is possible and can be visually appealing, allowing a wide seasonal spread of flowering, fruiting and foliage interest to be achieved. Careful choice of plants can considerably improve the ability to support biodiversity compared with a single plant species, as more food sources and niches are created in the same area for a longer period of time. The correct selection of compatible species is crucial as competition can result in some, more vigorous species overwhelming others. As a consequence, maintenance may be increased because of the need to cut back the growth of the more vigorous species.

13.3.3 Supports and fixings

A façade should be assessed for its ability to accommodate extra loads if a green wall is to be grown directly on to it, or where green wall support structure fixings are to be mounted. Supports for climbers need to be fixed securely to support the weight of the climber, plus wind and snow loading, and should be designed by a structural engineer.

Structural walls constructed from concrete and brick are usually ideal for attaching supports. Cladding is not, as it is not designed to be load bearing, although it may be possible to transfer loading to underlying structures behind the cladding using appropriate fixings. The simplest means of attaching supports for twining climbers to a building is the use vertical tensioned steel cables. If the bottom end is attached to an underground block of concrete, only the top end needs to be attached to the building, ie only a very small part of the exterior structure of the building needs to be load-bearing. A variety of other support systems using stainless or galvanised steel are available, and allow a somewhat wider range of plants to be utilised, eg Vines *Vitis spp.* and Clematis species. Safe installation of climber support systems needs the collaboration of a horticultural consultant with a structural engineer at the planning stage. The same considerations apply to health and safety as for green roofs (Section 11.3).

Figure 13.7

A vertical steel cable support system for a green wall (courtesy P Early)

Figure 13.8 *A metal framework provides support for climbing plants, which would otherwise not find anchorage on the smooth metal wall surface (courtesy P Early)*

Figure 13.9 *Traditional wooden trellis is possibly the most common method of supporting small green walls (courtesy P Early)*

Figure 13.10 *Steel cables provide horizontal support for a canopy over Regent Place car park entrance, London (courtesy P Early)*

Figure 3.11 *Steel cables are used to support climbing plants, which grow over a pedestrian walkway, IMAX, Waterloo, London (courtesy P Early)*

13.3.4 Root space for climbers

Generally, climbing plants are not difficult to grow and can be purchased from nurseries as plants, as seeds or as cuttings. Different climbing plant species are available to suit a variety of soil conditions. Strong growth is demanded of climbers for façade greening, and so deep fertile soils are needed, with a constant supply of moisture (although avoid water logging). High organic matter content helps to hold moisture and nutrients, so good soil preparation is very important, especially if the soil is thin or poor quality. In many cases the foundations of buildings limit root penetration. In itself this is not a problem if roots can find their way to better soil, but moisture does have to be available and there has to be a pocket of nutrient-rich soil to start the plants off. Root tunnels can be built into impervious areas, to assist roots in travelling to new areas of soil otherwise unavailable. Regular feeding may be needed as part of a maintenance programme if the underlying soil has low fertility.

Buildings often cast a rain shadow, exacerbating the drying effects of foundations. Initial irrigation may be necessary to ensure that plants get adequate moisture, at least until they get to a size when their roots penetrate into deeper soil layers. Mulches will also limit dry-season water loss, and can even be ornamental, as with the use of stones or pebbles. Drains should be located at a sufficient distance from the plants to avoid root penetration or suitable root barriers provided around the drains.

13.4 Structural considerations

The choice of which type of green wall system to use will, to some extent, depend upon the construction of the wall onto, or into, which it will be placed. Some wall constructions, such as curtain walling, do not generally provide a sufficiently robust surface upon which to secure green wall fixings unless these are designed and built-in at the construction phase. This does not eliminate the use of a green wall, but it does mean that alternatives, such as providing a freestanding structure, should be considered.

Freestanding structures or green wall anchoring systems that stand away from the wall surface may be the appropriate solution where the wall surface could be damaged by the chosen plant species or where access for wall maintenance is required.

When implementing hanging walls, care should be taken to ensure that parapets are strong enough to withstand the forces exerted by the plants.

13.5 Maintenance

It is a popular misconception that climbing plants damage the building fabric. This is only true where plants incompatible with the façade are grown, or plants are grown in areas that should be kept clear of vegetation. A lack of maintenance can also lead to plants damaging the fabric of the building. This is demonstrated in Figure 13.12 where the vegetation has covered the chimney pots, threatening the structure and presenting a safety hazard. In such circumstances the vegetation should be removed. Similarly in Figure 13.13 the cast iron drainpipe is providing the support for a twining climber. This uncontrolled growth could ultimately lead to the dangerous sudden collapse of the drainpipe.

Much of the German research into façade-greening has been concerned with minimising damage to buildings caused by the inappropriate use of climbers on traditional buildings. It needs to be stressed that contemporary buildings tend to offer far fewer opportunities for plants to cause damage because there tend to be fewer cracks and interstices in the fabric. An annual maintenance inspection is recommended to identify and rectify situations such as stems reaching beyond their supports, tangled or looping stems or damage to supports.

Figure 13.12 *Vegetation on chimney pots (courtesy P Early)*

Figure 13.13

Twining climber on a drainpipe (courtesy P Early)

Maintenance of vegetation may be required to avoid growth from obscuring windows and service ducts etc and to prevent the possibility of vegetation falling from the building due to excessive self-weight.

13.6 Costs

There is very limited information available on the costs of green walls. *Ivy Hedera spp.*, Virginia creeper *Parthenocissus quinquefolia*, climbing hydrangea *Hydrangea petiolaris*, and other self-supporting species do not need supports and therefore the costs incurred are minimal. For twining plants, support is required, so they are likely to be more expensive to install.

13.7 Assessment and monitoring

The success of a wall should be measured against the original design criteria. A site specific monitoring regime will be required if a formal assessment of the success of a scheme is needed.

Specific considerations include:

1. Has it achieved the original design intention?
2. Has it helped to meet any legislative requirements, BAP targets or planning conditions?
3. Is it being maintained to the required standard?
4. Are there any health and safety problems?
5. Is it enjoyed by people?

The monitoring regime that will be put in place depends on what the key performance indicators are as discussed for green roofs in Section 11.7.

Case study 15 Mur vegetaux (vegetated walls) of Patrick Blanc, France

Pershing Hall Paris (2001) (courtesy P Blanc)

Patrick Blanc is a botanist who has studied tropical-understorey plants, and is based at the National Centre for Scientific Research in Paris. He has developed a system to vegetate walls which was patented in 1988. Since then he has installed more than 80 vegetated walls.

His green wall system uses a (sometimes folded) waterproof plastic backing membrane covered with a water-retaining felt, supported by a steel frame. Variations in folds in the waterproof backing, the width of the wicking material and the rate of irrigation are used to create a variety of conditions for plants. A timer controls the supply of water and dissolved nutrients, which are pumped from a reservoir/sump. A large number of plants are individually planted into each wall to instantly create a densely vegetated screen.

The species used vary according to orientation and climate. The vegetated wall at the Chaumont-sur-Loire garden festival in 2005 used more than 13 exotic species as listed in the table below.

This technique appears to be mainly used for aesthetic purposes, but biodiversity benefits could be increased through the use of native species. These walls provide evaporative cooling and could be adapted to clean grey water.

Plants used at the Chaumont-sur-Loire Garden Festival vegetated wall 2005

Species	Origin
Begonia sutherlandii	South Africa
Cypella aquatica	South America
Ficus carica	Western Asia
Kirengeshoma palmate	Korea
Lonicera pileata	China
Raoulia australis	New Zealand
Sisyrinchium angustifolium	North America – naturalised in Britain
Erodium chammedryoïdes	Majorca
Saxifraga tricolor	China, Japan
Corydalis ochroleuca	Southern Europe
Lewisia cotyledon	American north-west
Pelargonium endlicherianum	South-west Turkey
Several moss species	

D Nestboxes and other complementary features

(courtesy J Pomroy)

14 NESTBOXES AND OTHER BIODIVERSITY FEATURES

14.1 Introduction

Nesting and roosting habitats for animals such as birds and bats are often a determining factor as to whether or not they can survive in a particular place. The increasingly tidy nature of our towns and cities means that such habitat is often in short supply, and in many instances is declining still further. Artificial nesting and roosting boxes can make an important contribution in providing alternative accommodation, enhancing the biodiversity value of buildings cheaply and easily.

Once there was just the bird box – a small wooden box with a sloping roof and a round hole big enough for a blue tit to squeeze through. Today, not only is there a whole host of bird boxes in a range of sizes, materials and dimensions to suit a wide variety of bird species, but there is a diverse range of bat boxes, along with structures for nesting bees, ladybirds, lacewings and other invertebrates. These can all make an important contribution to conserving and enhancing wild animals whether it be in the centre of an urban area or in the countryside. The majority of these boxes are designed to be attached to the exterior of a building or structure (Figures 14.1 and 14.2), and they can be retrofitted very easily. However, increasingly, nesting and roosting boxes are being manufactured for incorporation directly into a structure. These include bat tubes that provide a self maintaining roost integral to the wall; bat access panels that allow bats to access existing wall and roof voids; and nest "bricks" for swifts and house sparrows that are built into a wall.

These different nest boxes are complementary to green roofs and walls, and can provide nesting and roosting space for the species that the roofs and walls are designed to provide foraging habitat for.

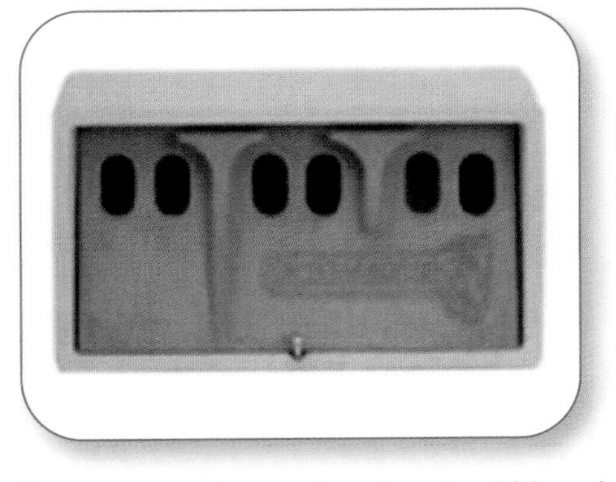

House sparrow terrace (courtesy Jacobi Jayne)

House martin nest box (courtesy Jacobi Jayne)

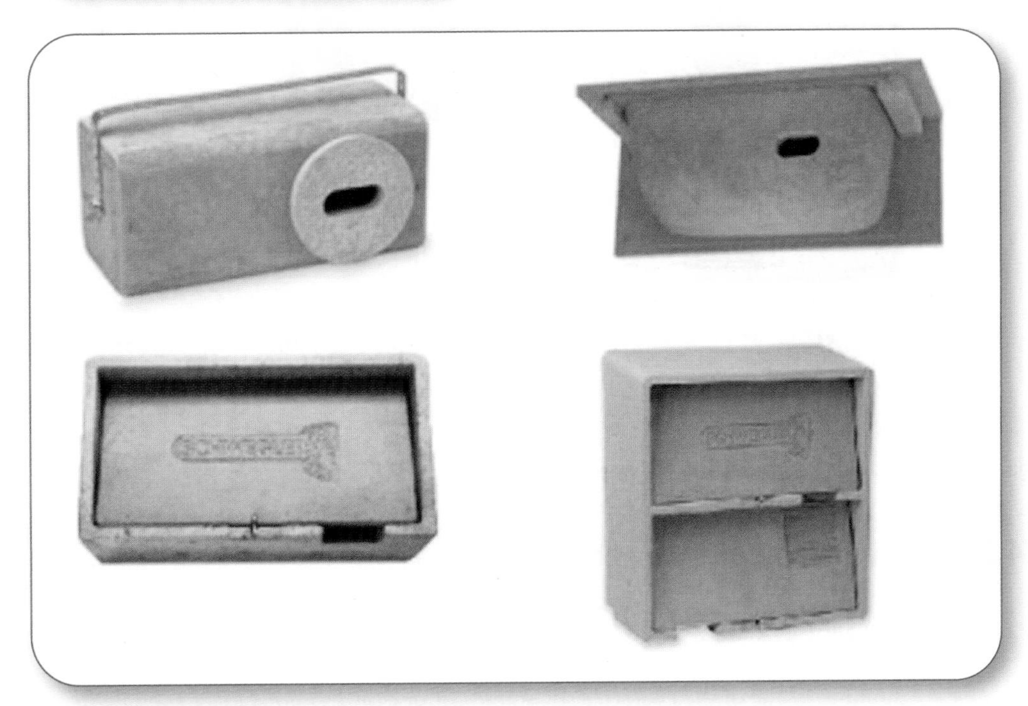

Various types of swift box for attaching to or building into a structure (courtesy Jacobi Jayne)

Figure 14.1 *Various boxes for a variety of species*

Brick box for redstarts

Brick box for pied wagtail and spotted flycatcher

Brick box for bats

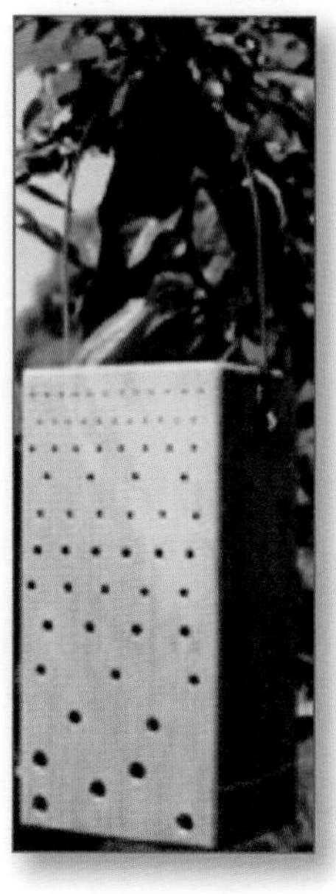

A wooden block for insects

A clay and reed box for insects

A box for ladybirds

Figure 14.2 *More boxes for a variety of species*

14.2 Swifts, swallows and martins

One bird species that is particularly threatened by the regeneration of our urban areas is the swift *Apus apus*. Swifts spend most of their life in the air; their screaming call overhead in the summer is one of the characteristic sounds of our towns and cities. Generally they depend on the voids in roof structures for nesting, but their survival is under threat as roof tiles are replaced with modern equivalents or with flat roofs which prevent their access. For example, swift colonies are being lost in Glasgow due to housing renovation and demolition. Surprisingly this is not as a result of the loss of old buildings, but often of houses that were built between the wars and just after, where a concrete lintel at the eaves seems to have provided the swifts with access to roof voids.

Fortunately swift nest boxes and nest bricks that can be built into walls, eaves and soffits are now widely available and in several different forms. These are self-contained and self-maintaining, and could be used on the most modern of buildings with no impact on the building's performance (Figure 14.5). It is possible to construct these from marine ply (Figures 14.3 and 14.4) or they can be bought ready made from materials such as a concrete and sawdust mix or similar. They should be installed at a minimum of 5 m above ground level and in a wall with a depth of 170 mm or more. A typical swift brick weighs 8.8 kg and once in position the outer face of the brick can be rendered or faced with brick or stone so that they appear inconspicuous on a façade (see Case study 14 and Figures 14.4 and 14.5). Ideally they should be used in groups as swifts are colony nesting birds. London's Swifts and Concern for Swifts have numerous examples of successful projects and provide advice on their websites <www.londons-swifts.org.uk> and <www.concernforswifts.com>.

It has been estimated by London's Swifts that to install 21 swift bricks in an office building would cost as little as £500. These boxes can be built into the walls of buildings, the structures of bridges or retaining walls, or even grouped around the top of structures such as lampposts or chimneys.

Figure 14.3 *Nest box designed by the joiner for a project in Glasgow (courtesy Concern for Swifts Scotland)*

Figure 14.4 *Nest box designed in co-operation with architects to replace swift nests lost due to demolition of buildings (courtesy Concern for Swifts Scotland)*

Figure 14.5 *Swift bricks set in brick work (courtesy Edward Mayer/London's Swifts)*

Figure 14.6 *14 swift boxes fitted under the eaves of an apartment block (courtesy Louis-Philippe Arnhem)*

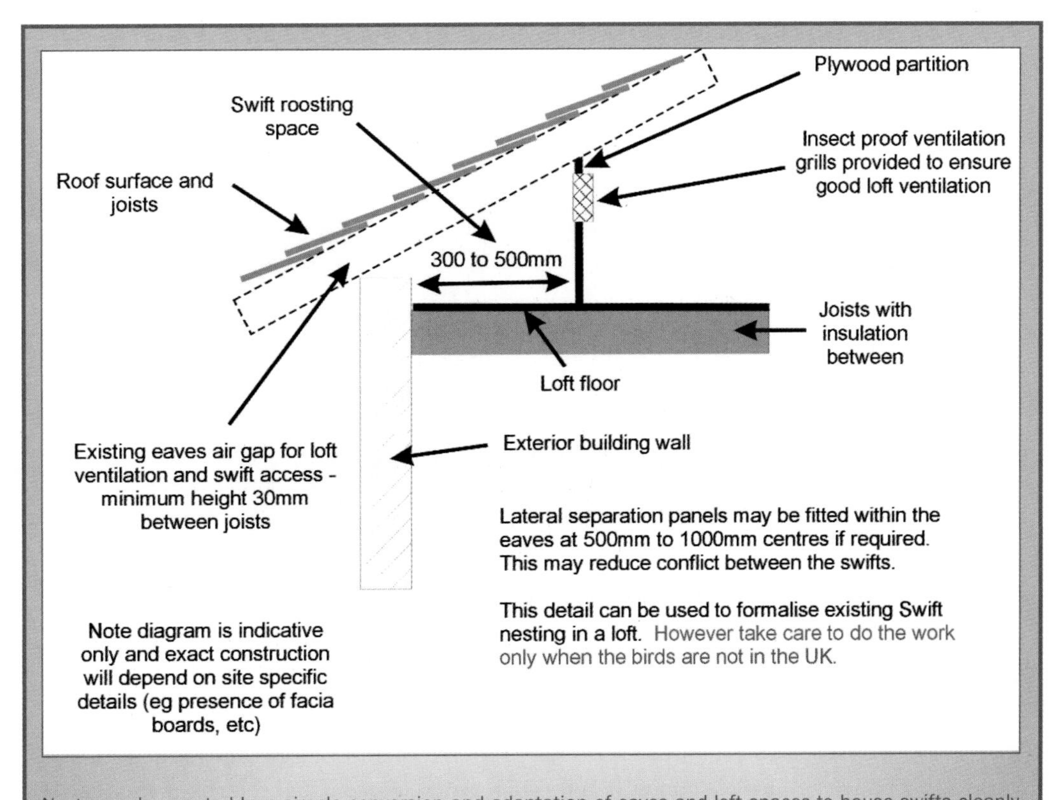
Plywood partition
Swift roosting space
Insect proof ventilation grills provided to ensure good loft ventilation
Roof surface and joists
300 to 500mm
Joists with insulation between
Loft floor
Existing eaves air gap for loft ventilation and swift access - minimum height 30mm between joists
Exterior building wall
Lateral separation panels may be fitted within the eaves at 500mm to 1000mm centres if required. This may reduce conflict between the swifts.
This detail can be used to formalise existing Swift nesting in a loft. However take care to do the work only when the birds are not in the UK.
Note diagram is indicative only and exact construction will depend on site specific details (eg presence of facia boards, etc)

Nests can be created by a simple conversion and adaptation of eaves and loft spaces to house swifts cleanly. This method can work on any suitable building. If heat loss is a problem then insulation boards can be laid down in the nest area to complement loose fibre glass laid in the non-nesting areas. Suitable nest place dimensions are 300 mm wide × 500 mm long × 200 mm high. A sloping roof of lesser height is acceptable as long as there is adequate space further back for the swifts to be able to stretch their wings. The entrance hole should ideally be 30 mm high × 65 mm long, round or oval, in either the base or side wall of the nest space, or else the existing eaves gap can be left as it is.

(Drawing after Edward Mayer/London's Swifts)

Be aware that refurbishment work to buildings - re-roofing, re-pointing, erection of scaffolding, etc can have a detrimental impact on nesting habitat for swifts. If carried out in the nesting season it can lead to disturbance and the possibility of young swifts or other hole nesting birds being bricked into walls - which is an offence under the Wildlife and Countryside Act (as amended) 1981.

14.3 Peregrine falcons

Peregrine falcons are now nesting regularly in towns and cities having recovered from the low populations of the 1960s. Artificial boxes and nesting trays for the species have been installed on a variety of buildings and structures throughout the UK to good effect. The boxes are situated as high on a building as possible; the higher the building the more likely it is that peregrines will use it. The nest boxes are substantial structures, measuring 450 × 600 × 900 mm, and need to be well attached to the building or structure on which they are to be sited. Nesting trays are simple box structures measuring 450 × 600 × 40 mm. Normally gravel or other substrate is laid inside the box or tray to a depth of about 20 mm. This provides a nesting scrape for the birds to lay their eggs into. The boxes should be placed on walls/ledges or in roof corners facing away from the prevailing winds. Where peregrines are already nesting on a building it can be beneficial to provide a nest tray. There are a number of examples where existing ledges that have been selected as nest sites have not been successful due to blocked drainage pipes causing flooding or, where there is a gentle slope, eggs rolling and breaking. The provision of a nest tray provides a secure and solid flat surface for the breeding peregrines.

Similar, although smaller, boxes have been successful for kestrels and owl species – the Hawk and Owl Trust have produced a useful booklet on the subject – Boxes, Baskets and Platforms – artificial nest sites for owls and other birds of prey (Dewar and Shawyer, 2001).

Figure 14.7 *Peregrine box and nest tray (courtesy D Morrison)*

14.4 House sparrows

House sparrows in urban areas have suffered catastrophic decline in their numbers over recent years, and the loss of nest sites through redevelopment and refurbishment may be partly responsible. Again nest boxes are available, specifically designed for the species, which provide for the colonial nesting of three or more pairs.

14.5 Other bird species

Other species of bird can benefit enormously from the erection of nest boxes on or within buildings (see Box 14.1). Robins, tits and other species, including black redstart, are catered for by a variety of either open fronted boxes or those with a hole in the front.

Box 14.1 *Selection of birds for which artificial nest boxes are suitable*

- house sparrows
- house martin
- sand martin (cliffs and steep banks)
- swallow
- swift
- tits
- robins
- wrens
- black redstart
- kestrel
- peregrine
- kingfisher (cliffs and steep banks)
- owls
- wagtails (eg grey wag boxes on bridges and other structures)
- dippers (bridges)
- jackdaw
- starling.

Boxes for insects include those for bees, lacewings, hornets and earwigs.

14.6 Bats

Bat populations have declined throughout the UK to the point where six of the 17 species that exist have been identified by the Government as needing special conservation help. Losses of roosting and foraging habitat have been major factors in this decline. Despite this, bats are still to be found in our towns and cities, where they are most likely to feed on insects over greenspace and wetland habitats. Their roosts can occur in a variety of places including buildings, old and modern, and in trees.

As detailed in Box 14.2 bats are protected by both UK and international law making it illegal to intentionally or recklessly damage, destroy or obstruct access to any place that a bat uses for shelter or protection, or that is a roosting place. However, finding bat roosts can be extremely difficult as the animals themselves are small and relatively inconspicuous. Suitable buildings should always be checked by a bat ecologist before works are carried out.

The law places an emphasis on the current conservation status of bats. However, in addition to this it is important to seek ways in which new bat roosts can be created and the opportunities for foraging increased. The biodiversity action plan process is one way in which this is taking place. A number of bat species are the subject of biodiversity action plans at both UK, regional and local levels and 70 or so local BAPs have an action plan for pipistrelle bats *Pipistrellus spp*.

For example, in the Greater Manchester biodiversity action plan the following objective has been set:

To maintain and wherever possible increase the size and number of current colonies – making the national target species, the pipistrelle, the main focus of initial action.

The London BAP has set the following objective and target:

Objective 3: *To protect and create new artificial roost sites in association with suitable feeding habitat.*

Target: *Establish 40 new roosting opportunities by 2006*

Buildings are commonly used by bats as roost sites throughout the year. They can squeeze through very small gaps; typically a gap 15–20 mm wide is large enough for a pipistrelle bat, and they can conceivably take advantage of normal architectural detail such as weather boarding, hanging tiles, gaps between soffits and walls, and holes in ventilation plates or air bricks. Designing such features into buildings or structures will increase the roosting opportunities for bats. However, a wide variety of purpose made bat boxes can be attached to the exterior of a building or within a roof void to which bats have access.

Bat boxes have been in use for many years with the first design published in France in 1918. Most designs are intended to replicate a tree hole, and are not dissimilar to a bird box except that, instead of having an open front or a hole, bat boxes have a slit of about 15–20 mm, usually placed underneath to permit bats to land and enter.

Bat boxes are used to varying degrees by all species of bat occurring in Britain with the exception of greater and lesser horseshoe bats and grey long-eared bats. Mostly bat boxes are occupied by solitary bats, small numbers of males or mating groups. However, the provision of artificial heating of larger bat boxes placed on the outside wall of houses has been shown to encourage their use by nursery colonies of species such as *pipistrelles* (Swift, 2004). The box is heated by an integral heating system with a roosting chamber physically separated from the mains-supplied electric coil heaters. A constant temperature of 27–28°C is maintained in the roosting chamber (Bat Conservation Trust, 2005).

An additional source of heat may also be required in space provided for bats within a roof void (Bat Conservation Trust, 2006). These "bat incubators" can encourage bats to stick to a certain part of the roof void by providing super-snug conditions and have proven especially beneficial for some of the rarer species such as greater horseshoe bats by also increasing survival rates (Bat Conservation Trust, 2005).

It is recommended that bat box schemes employ a mixture of different types of bat boxes (Swift, 2004).

In addition to stand-alone bat boxes it is now possible to obtain purpose built bat bricks and bat roosting units to build into walls. Bat bricks either provide slots for bats to roost in or provide access through walls to voids or roosting units. Bat access roof tiles are also available. These products are easy to install and can be well concealed within the façade of a building or structure.

An alternative solution to bat boxes is to enable bats to access existing or newly planned roof voids. If designed appropriately these can provide excellent facilities for a variety of bat species without causing any problems for human occupants of the building. Examples, of how this can be achieved are illustrated in Figure 14.8 and both English Nature (Mitchell-Jones, 2004) and Scottish Natural Heritage (Simpson and Brown, 1998) have produced guidance on these alternative solutions.

Figure 14.8 *Bat void in residential building (after Mitchell-Jones 2004)*

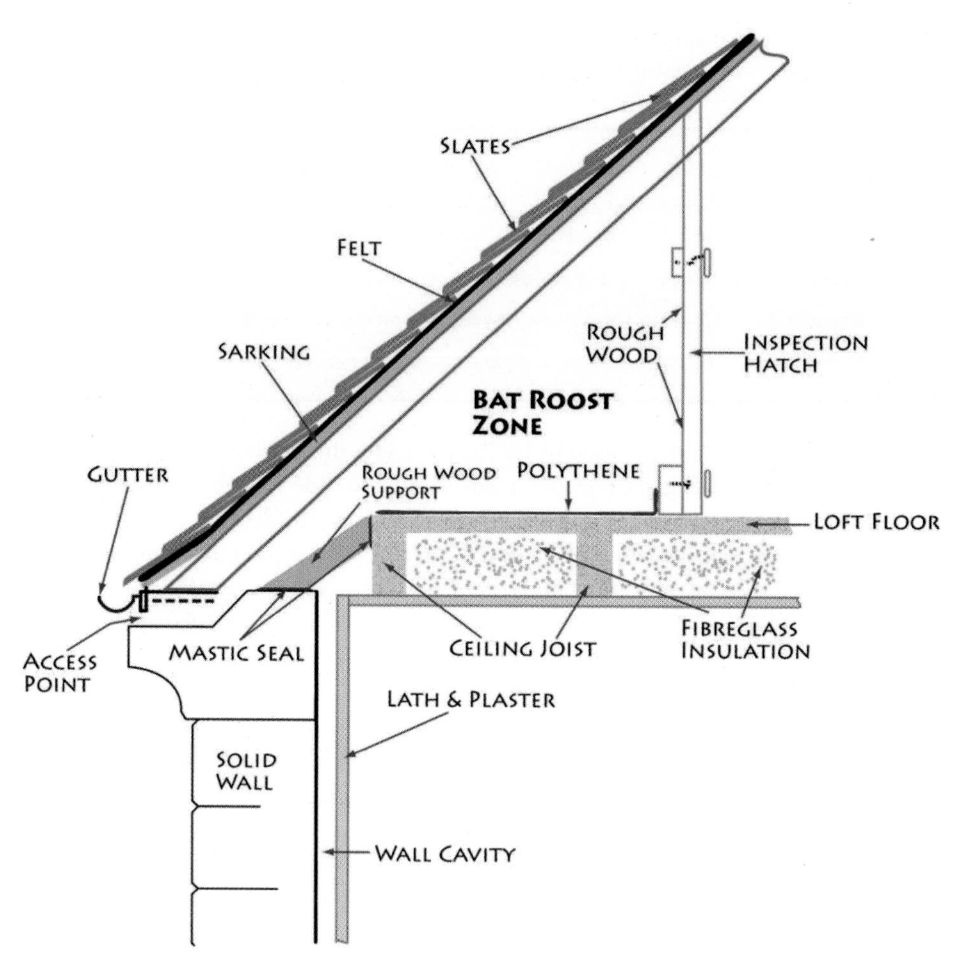

As more is learnt about bat ecology, so the sophistication of bat boxes increases. For example, it is known that, for maternity colonies, certain temperatures and humidity levels are critical. A number of heated bat boxes are now being installed including examples at Eastleigh in Hampshire, which replaced a roost lost due to a building demolition, (Hampshire Bat Group, 2006) and one installed by the Environment Agency in a pump house, with good results.

The positioning of bat boxes is critical to their success. Bats are dependant for their survival on habitat that will supply them with an abundant supply of insects. Thus, a box or other facility in the middle of a densely urban environment is unlikely to be successful, whereas similar features that are adjacent to a watercourse or that link with a matrix of tree, scrub and grassland habitats are far more likely to be used by bats. Green roofs and in particular walls will provide useful enhancements to existing bat habitat, and together with the provision of bat boxes and other roosting facilities will make a positive contribution to bat conservation in our towns and cities.

Box 14.2 *Bats and the law*

The Wildlife and Countryside Act 1981 (WCA) protects bats and their roosts in England, Scotland and Wales. Some parts have been amended by the Countryside and Rights of Way Act 2000 (CRoW) which applies only in England and Wales, and by the Nature Conservation (Scotland) Act 2004 which applies in Scotland. Similar provisions for Northern Ireland are contained within the Wildlife (Northern Ireland) Order 1985.

The Conservation (Natural Habitats, &c.) Regulations 1994 (better known as the Habitats Regulations) implement the EU Council Directive on the Conservation of Natural Habitats and of Wild Fauna and Flora – better known as the Habitats Directive. All bats are listed as "European protected species of animals".

The protection afforded to bats makes it an offence among other things to:

- intentionally or recklessly damage, destroy or obstruct access to any place that a bat uses for shelter or protection. This is taken to mean all bat roosts whether bats are present or not
- intentionally or recklessly disturb a bat while it is occupying a structure or place that it uses for shelter or protection.

In cases where buildings are to be demolished or renovated and a bat roost is already present, then no works will be able to proceed until a licence from the Department for Environment, Food and Rural Affairs (or its equivalent in Wales, Scotland and Northern Ireland) has been obtained. The licence will only be granted once full mitigation for the damage or loss of any roost has been guaranteed in the form of a detailed method statement. Mitigation can take the form of purpose built bat "hotels" that are designed as stand-alone structures or, more frequently, the inclusion of features such bat boxes or bat bricks either internally or externally to the building.

When bats may potentially be an issue contact the Bat Conservation trust for further advice.

Figure 14.9

Bats leaving a wall mounted bat box (courtesy J Goldsmith)

Figure 14.10

Natterer's bat leaving a purpose made Norfolk bat brick (courtesy J Goldsmith)

14.7 Invertebrates

Insects and other invertebrates are an essential element of the natural environment whether it be in town or in the country. They pollinate flowers, are a source of food for birds and other animals, and help to tidy up dead and waste organic material. However, their usefulness has not guaranteed their survival and many species are now under threat of extinction. Two species of bumblebee became extinct in the 20th century and populations of the other species have fallen dramatically over the past fifty years. One of the reasons for this decline has been the changes in farming methods, resulting in far fewer foraging areas for bumblebees.

As with birds and bats the provision of boxes can help a range of beneficial invertebrates to survive. Bumblebee boxes are similar in size to a small bird box but they have two compartments: one in which the queen breeds that is filled with wood shavings, and one where the other bees live. Boxes for red mason bees or leafcutter bees, both of which are non aggressive and excellent for pollinating plants, comprise a series of tubes. The bees lay their eggs in tubes, one at a time, each with a supply of pollen or nectar, and a plug of mud between them. Insulated compartments within the same boxes are used by over wintering ladybirds and lacewings (both natural predators of Aphids that are harmful to plants).

As previously mentioned in Section 6.4 the value of brownfield sites for invertebrates, especially bumblebees, is increasingly recognised. The provision of extensive green roof habitat along with artificial nesting and hibernating sites can provide a small, but important contribution to halting the decline in the populations of these beautiful and important species. It also demonstrates how by using green roofs, walls and boxes as part of a more strategic framework, the benefits of this synergistic approach are greater than the sum of the individual parts.

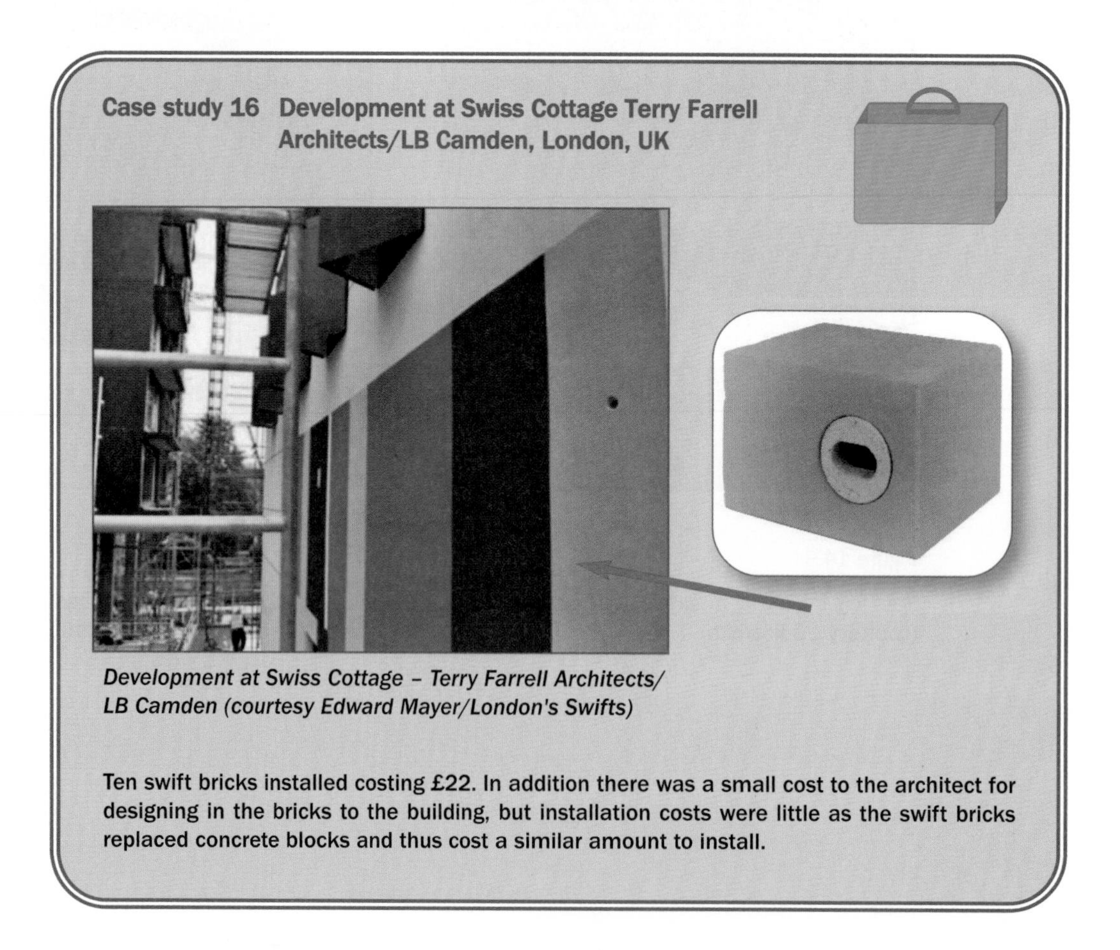

Case study 16 Development at Swiss Cottage Terry Farrell Architects/LB Camden, London, UK

Development at Swiss Cottage – Terry Farrell Architects/ LB Camden (courtesy Edward Mayer/London's Swifts)

Ten swift bricks installed costing £22. In addition there was a small cost to the architect for designing in the bricks to the building, but installation costs were little as the swift bricks replaced concrete blocks and thus cost a similar amount to install.

Case study 17 Bat box on Forestry Commission building, Norfolk, UK

Bat box on Forestry Commission building, Norfolk (courtesy Cambridge Bat Group)

Specially designed large boxes approximately 1 m wide and slightly taller, by about 100 mm deep have been successfully used as mitigation over the past decade. These boxes are coloured dark brown or black, and face into the sun in order to get warm enough to attract breeding bats. Internally they should contain a number of partitions with internal linkage to be successful. The one illustrated above was placed on the timber wall of a Forestry Commission building in East Anglia in 1992 as mitigation for the loss of roosting space during the repair of a timber cavity wall and has been used every year since by up to 150 pipistrelles – the most ever recorded in a UK bat box. It has even been used by pipistrelles for hibernating, as well as a mating roost in the autumn.

Another box of similar design was used as mitigation adjacent to an East Anglian water mill when a Pipistrelle colony was being excluded under licence. This has been used by a breeding colony of over 100 pipistrelles almost every year since 1994. Noctules, two pipistrelle species, brown long-eared and Natterer's bats have all used this style of box.

Examples are now illustrated on a number of web pages such as: <www.norfolk-bat-group.org.uk/framebb.html> (Norfolk Bat Group, 2003).

Nestboxes and other biodiversity features: Key points

- nesting and roosting habitats for animals such as birds and bats are often a determining factor as to whether or not they can survive in a particular place
- artificial nesting and roosting boxes can make an important contribution in providing alternative accommodation, enhancing the biodiversity value of buildings cheaply and easily
- there is a whole host of bird boxes in a range of sizes, materials and dimensions to suit a wide variety of bird species, and a diverse range of bat boxes, along with structures for nesting bees, ladybirds, lacewings and other invertebrates
- increasingly, nesting and roosting boxes are being manufactured for incorporation directly into a structure (eg swift bricks) with no impact on the building's performance
- nesting and roosting boxes are complementary to green roofs and walls and can provide nesting and roosting space for the species that the roofs and walls are designed to provide habitat for
- an alternative solution to bat boxes is to enable bats to access existing or newly planned roof voids
- the positioning of bat boxes is critical to their success. Bats require an abundant supply of insects. Boxes adjacent to a watercourse or that link with a matrix of tree, scrub and grassland habitats are far more likely to be used by bats. Green roofs and walls will provide useful enhancements to existing bat habitat
- the Wildlife and Countryside Act 1981 protects many species including swifts and bats and their roosts in England, Scotland and Wales. Ensure that any work does not contravene the provisions in the Act. It is illegal, among other things, to intentionally or recklessly damage, destroy or obstruct access to any place that a bat uses for shelter or protection, or that is a roosting place.

APPENDICES

A1 EXTRACTS FROM NATIONAL PLANNING POLICIES WHICH ENCOURAGE THE IMPLEMENTATION OF GREEN ROOFS AND WALLS

Planning Policy Statement 1: General policy and principles (2005)

Introduction	1	Planning shapes the places where people live and work and the country we live in. Good planning ensures that we achieve the right development, in the right place and at the right time. It makes a positive difference to people's lives and helps to deliver homes, jobs and better opportunities for all, while protecting and enhancing the natural and historic environment, and conserving the countryside and open spaces that are vital resources for everyone.
Sustainable development	3	Sustainable development is the core principle underpinning planning. At the heart of sustainable development is the simple idea of ensuring a better quality of life for everyone, now and for future generations. A widely used definition was drawn up by the World Commission on environment and development in 1987: *"development that meets the needs of the present without compromising the ability of future generations to meet their own needs."*
Protection and enhancement of the environment	17	The Government is committed to protecting and enhancing the quality of the natural and historic environment, in both rural and urban areas. Planning policies should seek to protect and enhance the quality, character and amenity value of the countryside and urban areas as a whole. A high level of protection should be given to most valued townscapes and landscapes, wildlife habitats and natural resources. Those with national and international designations should receive the highest level of protection.
	18	The condition of our surroundings has a direct impact on the quality of life, and the conservation and improvement of the natural and built environment brings social and economic benefit for local communities. Planning should seek to maintain and improve the local environment and help to mitigate the effects of declining environmental quality through positive policies on issues such as design, conservation and the provision of public space.
Delivering sustainable development	27 (ix)	In preparing development plans, planning authorities should seek to: Enhance as well as protect biodiversity, natural habitats, the historic environment and landscape and townscape character.
Design	34	Planning authorities should plan positively for the achievement of high quality and inclusive design for all development, including individual buildings, public and private spaces and wider area development schemes. Good design should contribute positively to making places better for people. Design which is inappropriate in its context, or which fails to take the opportunities available for improving the character and quality of an area and the way it functions, should not be accepted.

This umbrella guidance for the Government's planning policies establishes the principles and context for planning in England. The following are of interest in relation to green roofs and walls, and promoting biodiversity in and on buildings:

Planning Policy Statement 3: Housing (2006)

<table>
<tr><td rowspan="1">Strategic housing policy objectives</td><td>9</td><td>The Government's key housing policy goal is to ensure that everyone has the opportunity of living in a decent home, which they can afford, in a community where they want to live. To achieve this, the Government is seeking:
◆ to achieve a wide choice of high quality homes, both affordable and market housing, to address the requirements of the community
◆ to widen opportunities for home ownership and ensure high quality housing for those who cannot afford market housing, in particular those who are vulnerable or in need
◆ to improve affordability across the housing market by increasing the supply of housing
◆ to create sustainable, inclusive, mixed communities in all areas, both urban and rural.</td></tr>
<tr><td>Achieving high quality housing</td><td>12</td><td>Good design is fundamental to the development of high quality new housing, which contributes to the creation of sustainable, mixed communities.</td></tr>
<tr><td>Designing for quality</td><td>13</td><td>Reflecting policy in PPS1, good design should contribute positively to making places better for people. Design which is inappropriate in its context, or which fails to take the opportunities available for improving the character and quality of an area and the way it functions, should not be accepted.</td></tr>
<tr><td rowspan="3"></td><td>14</td><td>Local planning authorities should develop a shared vision with their local communities of the type(s) of residential environments they wish to see and develop design policies that set out the quality of development that will be expected for the local area, aimed at:
◆ creating places, streets and spaces which meet the needs of people, are visually attractive, safe, accessible, functional, inclusive, have their own distinctive identity and maintain and improve local character
◆ promoting designs and layouts which make efficient and effective use of land, including encouraging innovative approaches to help deliver high quality outcomes.</td></tr>
<tr><td>15</td><td>Local planning authorities should encourage applicants to bring forward sustainable and environmentally friendly new housing developments, including affordable housing developments, and in doing so should reflect the approach set out in the forthcoming PPS on climate change, including the Code for Sustainable Homes.</td></tr>
<tr><td>16</td><td>Matters to consider when assessing design quality include the extent to which the proposed development:
◆ is easily accessible and well-connected to public transport and community facilities and services, and is well laid out so that all the space is used efficiently, is safe, accessible and user-friendly
◆ provides, or enables good access to community, and green and open amenity and recreational space (including play space) as well as private outdoor space such as residential gardens, patios and balconies
◆ is well integrated with, and complements, the neighbouring buildings and the local area more generally in terms of scale, density, layout and access
◆ facilitates the efficient use of resources, during construction and in use, and seeks to adapt to and reduce the impact of, and on, climate change.
◆ takes a design-led approach to the provision of car-parking space, that is well-integrated with a high quality public realm and streets that are pedestrian, cycle and vehicle friendly
◆ creates, or enhances, a distinctive character that relates well to the surroundings and supports a sense of local pride and civic identity
◆ provides for the retention or re-establishment of the biodiversity within residential environments.</td></tr>
</table>

Planning Policy Statement 9: Biodiversity and Geological Conservation (2005)

<table>
<tr><td>Key principles</td><td>1</td><td>Regional planning bodies and local planning authorities should adhere to the following key principles to ensure that the potential impacts of planning decisions on biodiversity and geological conservation are fully considered:

i Development plan policies and planning decisions should be based upon up-to-date information about the environmental characteristics of their areas. These characteristics should include the relevant biodiversity and geological resources of the area. In reviewing environmental characteristics local authorities should assess the potential to sustain and enhance those resources.
ii Plan policies and planning decisions should aim to maintain, and enhance, restore or add to biodiversity and geological conservation interests. In taking decisions, local planning authorities should ensure that appropriate weight is attached to designated sites of international, national and local importance; protected species; and to biodiversity and geological interests within the wider environment.
iii Plan policies on the form and location of development should take a strategic approach to the conservation, enhancement and restoration of biodiversity and geology, and recognise the contributions that sites, areas and features, both individually and in combination, make to conserving these resources.
iv Plan policies should promote opportunities for the incorporation of beneficial biodiversity and geological features within the design of development.
v Development proposals where the principal objective is to conserve or enhance biodiversity and geological conservation interests should be permitted.
vi The aim of planning decisions should be to prevent harm to biodiversity and geological conservation interests. Where granting planning permission would result in significant harm to those interests, local planning authorities will need to be satisfied that the development cannot reasonably be located on any alternative sites that would result in less or no harm. In the absence of any such alternatives, local planning authorities should ensure that, before planning permission is granted, adequate mitigation measures are put in place. Where a planning decision would result in significant harm to biodiversity and geological interests, which cannot be prevented or adequately mitigated against, appropriate compensation measures should be sought. If that significant harm cannot be prevented, adequately mitigated against, or compensated for, then planning permission should be refused.</td></tr>
<tr><td>Regional spatial strategies</td><td>2</td><td>Regional planning bodies should liaise closely with regional biodiversity flora or equivalent bodies, English Nature or its successors and the Environment Agency to identify the current regional and sub-regional distribution of priority habitats and species, internationally and nationally designated areas, and broad areas for habitat restoration and re-creation. Regional planning bodies should liaise with the British Geological Survey and, where appropriate, local regionally important geological/geomorphological sites groups on geodiversity issues. Over time the distribution of habitats and species, and geomorphological processes and features, will be affected by climate change and such change will need to be taken into account.</td></tr>
<tr><td></td><td>3</td><td>Regional spatial strategies should:

i Incorporate biodiversity objectives.
ii Address regional, sub-regional and cross-boundary issues in relation to habitats, species and geomorphological processes through criteria-based policies.
iii Include policies to conserve and enhance biodiversity at the regional and sub-regional levels.
iv Include targets for the restoration and re-creation of priority habitats and the recovery of priority species populations, linked to national goals.
v Identify suitable indicators for monitoring biodiversity.</td></tr>
</table>

Local development frameworks	**4** Local authorities should take an integrated approach to planning for biodiversity and geodiversity when preparing local development documents. They should ensure that policies in local development documents reflect, and are consistent with, national, regional and local biodiversity priorities and objectives (including those agreed by local biodiversity partnerships).
	5 Local development frameworks should: i Indicate the location of designated sites of importance for biodiversity and geodiversity, making clear distinctions between the hierarchy of international, national, regional and locally designated sites. ii Identify any areas or sites for the restoration or creation of new priority habitats which contribute to regional targets, and support this restoration or creation through appropriate policies. References to regional spatial strategies in this policy statement also apply to the *Spatial Development Strategy for Greater London*, also known as the "London Plan".
	Networks of natural habitats **12** Networks of natural habitats provide a valuable resource. They can link sites of biodiversity importance and provide routes or stepping stones for the migration, dispersal and genetic exchange of species in the wider environment. Local authorities should aim to maintain networks by avoiding or repairing the fragmentation and isolation of natural habitats through policies in plans. Such networks should be protected from development, and, where possible, strengthened by or integrated within it. This may be done as part of a wider strategy for the protection and extension of open space and access routes such as canals and rivers, including those within urban areas.
	Previously developed land **13** The re-use of previously developed land for new development makes a major contribution to sustainable development by reducing the amount of countryside and undeveloped land that needs to be used. However, where such sites have significant biodiversity or geological interest of recognised local importance, local planning authorities, together with developers, should aim to retain this interest or incorporate it into any development of the site.
	Biodiversity within developments **14** Development proposals provide many opportunities for building-in beneficial biodiversity or geological features as part of good design. When considering proposals, local planning authorities should maximise such opportunities in and around developments, using planning obligations where appropriate.
	Species protection **15** Many individual wildlife species receive statutory protection under a range of legislative provisions, and specific policies in respect of these species should not be included in local development documents (see also Part IV of ODPM/Defra Circular, ODPM 06/2005, Defra 01/2005).
	16 Other species have been identified as requiring conservation action as species of principal importance for the conservation of biodiversity in England. Local authorities should take measures to protect the habitats of these species from further decline through policies in local development documents. Planning authorities should ensure that these species are protected from the adverse effects of development, where appropriate, by using planning conditions or obligations. Planning authorities should refuse permission where harm to the species or their habitats would result unless the need for, and benefits of, the development clearly outweigh that harm.

Planning for biodiversity and geological conservation – a guide to good practice (2006)

Building in biodiversity	**5.32** PPS9 states that plan policies should promote opportunities for the incorporation of beneficial biodiversity and geological conservation features within the design of development. The design, layout and landscaping of new developments offer enormous opportunities to add to, or enhance, biodiversity or geological conservation. These can range from minor additions to the fabric of buildings, for example to provide nesting spaces for species such as swifts (see below), through to providing major new areas of biodiversity habitat alongside development. The type of measures introduced may be guided by priorities established in local and regional BAPs.
	5.33 The England Biodiversity Strategy makes specific reference to the need to incorporate more biodiversity elements into buildings and uses the "green roofs for black redstarts" work in London as a case study. Green roof initiatives provide a prominent example of incorporating biodiversity in the design of new buildings. London, for example, has a number of green roofs which have attracted particular attention. The Laban Dance Centre, winner of the Stirling Prize for Architecture 2003, has an aggregate-based roof created for black redstarts from building rubble on site.
	5.34 Other species, such as bats and swifts, are highly dependent on built structures for survival. Maintenance of existing and the design of new buildings can take account of this. Biodiversity can be incorporated into small-scale developments through wildlife-friendly landscaping, installation of sustainable drainage schemes, and features such as green walls, balconies, roofs and nesting, and roosting spaces.
	5.35 At a simple level, nest and roosting boxes can be easily incorporated in or onto existing and new buildings. A wide range of boxes to benefit birds, bats and some invertebrates are available. There are also opportunities for incorporating artificial nesting burrows in the walls and embankments of civil engineering structures to benefit species such as the sand martin and kingfisher.
	5.36 Development control decisions which embrace biodiversity and geological conservation can be of broad benefit to communities by creating employment through new projects, creating cost effective naturally functioning utilities (such as for flood relief and drainage), enhancing the local economy through tourism and improving local surroundings which enhance quality of life.

Planning Policy Statement 11: Regional Spatial Strategies (2004)

The sustainability appraisal	**2.37** Sustainability appraisal is based on the four aims for sustainable development outlined in Planning Policy Statement 1: ◆ social progress which recognises the needs of everyone ◆ effective protection of the environment ◆ the prudent use of natural resources ◆ maintenance of high and stable levels of economic growth and employment. It should ensure that these four aims are tackled in an integrated way, in line with the principles for sustainable development set out in the Government's sustainable development strategy *"A better qualify of life – a strategy for sustainable development in the UK"*.
Annex A: Policy and guidance on topics to be covered in a RSS	Includes a list of EU, central government or central government agency national policies, guidance, research and related material dealing with biodiversity and nature conservation, climate change, water and energy that should be taken into account when RPBs are preparing revisions to Regional Spatial Strategies.

Planning Policy Statement 25: Development and flood risk (2006)

Key planning objectives	5	The aims of planning policy on development and flood risk are to ensure that flood risk is taken into account at all stages in the planning process to avoid inappropriate development in areas at risk of flooding, and to direct development away from areas at highest risk. Where new development is exceptionally necessary in such areas, policy aims to make it safe without increasing flood risk elsewhere and where possible, reducing flood risk overall.
	6	Regional planning bodies (RPBs) and local planning authorities (LPAs) should prepare and implement planning strategies that help to deliver sustainable development by: **Appraising risk** ◆ identifying land at risk and the degree of risk of flooding from river, sea and other sources in their areas ◆ preparing Regional Flood Risk Appraisals (RFRAs) or Strategic Flood Risk Assessments (SFRAs) as appropriate, as freestanding assessments that contribute to the sustainability appraisal of their plans. **Managing risk** ◆ framing policies for the location of development which avoid flood risk to people and property where possible, and manage any residual risk, taking account of the impacts of climate change ◆ only permitting development in areas of flood risk when there are no reasonably available sites in areas of lower flood risk, and benefits of the development outweigh the risks from flooding. **Reducing risk** ◆ safeguarding land from development that is required for current and future flood management eg conveyance and storage of flood water, and flood defences ◆ reducing flood risk to and from new development through location, layout and design, incorporating sustainable drainage systems (SUDS) ◆ using opportunities offered by new development to reduce the causes and impacts of flooding eg surface water management plans; making the most of the benefits of green infrastructure for flood storage, conveyance and SUDS; re-creating functional floodplain; and setting back defences. **A partnership approach** ◆ working effectively with the Environment Agency, other operating authorities and other stakeholders to ensure that best use is made of their expertise and information so that plans are effective and decisions on planning applications can be delivered expeditiously ◆ ensuring spatial planning supports flood risk management policies and plans, river basin management plans and emergency planning.
Annex F: Managing Surface Water The effect of development	F3	The effect of development is generally to reduce the permeability of at least part of the site. This markedly changes the site's response to rainfall. Without specific measures, the volume of water that runs off the site and the peak runoff flow rate is likely to increase. Inadequate surface water drainage arrangements in new development can threaten the development itself and increase the risk of flooding to others.
	F4	To satisfactorily manage flood risk in new development, appropriate surface water drainage arrangements are required, to manage surface water and the impact of the natural water cycle on people and property.
	F6	Surface water arising from a developed site should, as far as is practicable, be managed in a sustainable manner to mimic the surface water flows arising from the site prior to the proposed development, while reducing the flood risk to the site itself and elsewhere, taking climate change into account. This should be demonstrated as part of the flood risk assessment.

	F7	The term sustainable drainage systems (SUDS) is frequently used and taken in this PPS to cover the whole range of sustainable approaches to surface water drainage management including: ◆ source control measures including rainwater recycling and drainage ◆ infiltration devices to allow water to soak into the ground, that can include individual soakaways and communal facilities ◆ filter strips and swales, which are vegetated features that hold and drain water downhill mimicking natural drainage patterns ◆ filter drains and porous pavements to allow rainwater and runoff to infiltrate into permeable material below ground and provide storage if needed ◆ basins and ponds to hold excess water after rain and allow controlled discharge that avoids flooding.
Surface water drainage and sustainable drainage systems (SUDS)		
	F10	The surface water drainage arrangements for any development site should be such that the volumes and peak flow rates of surface water leaving a developed site are no greater than the rates prior to the proposed development, unless specific off-site arrangements are made and result in the same net effect.
	F11	For new development, it may be necessary to provide surface water storage and infiltration to limit and reduce both the peak rate of discharge from the site and the total volume discharged from the site. There may be circumstances where it is appropriate for infiltration attenuation storage to be provided outside the development site, if necessary through the use of a Section 106 agreement.

Chapter 4 *Managing surface water* Sustainable drainage systems	**4.10** SUDS aim to mimic natural drainage processes and remove pollutants from urban runoff at source. SUDS comprise a wide range of techniques, including green roofs, permeable paving, rainwater harvesting, swales, detention basins, ponds and wetlands. To realise the greatest improvement in water quality and flood risk management these components should be used in combination, often referred to as the SUDS management train.
	4.11 PPS1: Delivering sustainable development and PPS25 require that Regional Planning Bodies (RPBs) and LPAs should promote SUDS. To comply with the requirements of PPS25, Regional Spatial Strategies (RSSs) should include specific policies to encourage sustainable drainage practices. RFRAs should include a broad-scale consideration of surface water management, focusing on regionally-specific issues. LPAs should ensure policies encourage sustainable drainage practices in their LDDs. Priority should be given to the use of infiltration drainage techniques as opposed to discharging surface water to watercourses. Where infiltration techniques are not viable, discharging site runoff to watercourses is preferable to the use of sewers. A number of LPAs have developed supplementary planning documents that set out the principles of SUDS and provide guidance on how they would expect to see sustainable drainage accommodated in a development. SFRAs should identify the potential issues associated with drainage of key site allocations and provide an indication of the types of measure which may be appropriate, taking account of location, site opportunities and constraints and geology. In this way developers will be able to factor the surface water management of a proposed development into their considerations of available sites at an early stage.
Land take	**4.14** Some SUDS techniques require significant land take, although techniques such as green roofs and permeable pavements can be used in high-density urban developments. There may also be opportunities to make dual use of greenspace areas within the development. HR Wallingford's Use of SUDS in high density developments looks at approaches to overcome this challenge.
Incorporating environmental improvements	**4.23** When fully integrated into the design and landscaping of a development, SUDS can significantly improve environmental quality. Those promoting new developments should encourage infrastructure engineers to work closely with planners and architects from the earliest stages of projects to ensure that wider opportunities are not missed.

Table 4.2 Some environmental benefits of SUDS

Feature	Environmental benefit
Green roofs	Attenuated run-off, improved aesthetics, climate change adaptation.
Water butts	Attenuated run-off, water conservation.
Porous and pervious paving	Infiltration to promote attenuation and groundwater recharge, treatment by detention, treatment by filtration.
Rainwater harvesting	Attenuated run-off, water conservation.
Filter strips	Green links/corridors through a development, run-off attenuation, filtering of contaminants.
Swales	Can be planted with trees and shrubs, provides green links/corridors, improved visual amenity, conveyance of storm water.
Infiltration basins	Potentially compatible with dual-use eg sports pitches, play areas, wildlife habitat. Can be any shape – curving or irregular – with scope for improved visual amenity. Treatment by detention and filtration.
Detention basins	Can be designed as an amenity or wildlife habitat. Treatment by detention.
Retention ponds	Open water bodies which can significantly enhance the visual amenity of a development. Treatment by detention. Wildlife habitat. Fishing, boating and other water sports. Can abstract water for re-use – eg irrigation.
Wetlands	Provide a range of habitats for plants and wildlife. Biological treatment linear wetlands can also provide green corridors.

The London Plan (2004)

The Spatial Development Strategy for London has reflected the emerging interest in green roofs by their specific mention and inferred reference in a couple of policy supporting paragraphs. The *Supplementary Planning Guidance on Sustainable Design & Construction* was published in 2006.

Policy 4B.6: *Sustainable design and construction*	The Mayor will, and boroughs should, ensure future developments meet the highest standards of sustainable design and construction and reflect this principle in UDP policies. These will include measures to: ◆ re-use land and buildings ◆ conserve energy, materials, water and other resources ◆ ensure designs make the most of natural systems both within and around the building ◆ reduce the impacts of noise, pollution, flooding and micro-climatic effects ◆ ensure developments are comfortable and secure for users ◆ conserve and enhance the natural environment, particularly in relation to biodiversity ◆ promote sustainable waste behaviour in new and existing developments, including support for local integrated recycling schemes, CHP schemes and other treatment options (subject to Policy 4A.1 and 4A.2) ◆ applications for strategic developments should include a statement showing how sustainability principles will be met in terms of demolition, construction and long-term management ◆ boroughs should ensure that, where appropriate, the same sustainability principles are used to assess planning applications.
	4.52 Sustainable design and construction can reduce the consumption of resources, cut greenhouse gases and contribute to the good health of Londoners. Sustainable design is based on principles that are intended to ensure that buildings are efficient in resource use, recognise the uniqueness of locations, are healthy, adaptable and responsible in protecting the environment and make the most of natural systems including, for example the use of passive solar design or local ecosystems. Several of these issues are addressed through Building Regulation requirements and other procedures. This policy should sit alongside those requirements. The Mayor will work with partners to produce Supplementary Planning Guidance and to provide further information on relevant aspirational targets.
Policy 4B.9: *Large-scale buildings – design and impact*	All large-scale buildings including tall buildings should be of the highest quality design and in particular: ◆ meet the requirements of the View Protection Framework set out in Policy 4B.15 of this plan ◆ be suited to their wider context in terms of proportion and composition and in terms of their relationship to other buildings, streets, public and private open spaces, the waterways or other townscape elements ◆ illustrate exemplary standards of sustainable construction and resource management and potential for renewable energy generation and recycling ◆ be sensitive to their impact on micro-climates in terms of wind, sun, reflection and overshadowing ◆ pay particular attention, in residential environments, to privacy, amenity and overshadowing.
Policy 3D.12: *Biodiversity and nature conservation*	The Mayor will work with partners to ensure a proactive approach to the protection, promotion and management of biodiversity in support of the Mayor's biodiversity strategy. The planning of new development and regeneration should have regard to nature conservation and biodiversity, and opportunities should be taken to achieve positive gains for conservation through the form and design of development. Where appropriate, measures may include creating, enhancing and managing wildlife habitat and natural landscape. Priority for habitat creation should be given to sites which assist in achieving the targets in biodiversity action plans (BAPs) and sites within or near to areas deficient in accessible wildlife sites.

Policy 3D.12: *Biodiversity and nature conservation*	The Mayor will work with partners to ensure a proactive approach to the protection, promotion and management of biodiversity in support of the Mayor's biodiversity strategy. The planning of new development and regeneration should have regard to nature conservation and biodiversity, and opportunities should be taken to achieve positive gains for conservation through the form and design of development. Where appropriate, measures may include creating, enhancing and managing wildlife habitat and natural landscape. Priority for habitat creation should be given to sites which assist in achieving the targets in biodiversity action plans (BAPs) and sites within or near to areas deficient in accessible wildlife sites.
	Where development is proposed which would affect a site of importance for nature conservation, the approach should be to seek to avoid adverse impact on the nature conservation value of the site, and if that is not possible, to minimise such impact and seek mitigation of any residual impacts. Where, exceptionally, development is to be permitted because the reasons for it are judged to outweigh significant harm to nature conservation, appropriate compensation should be sought.
	3.258 The Mayor expects the biodiversity and natural heritage of London to be conserved and enhanced for the benefit of this and future generations. He will assist boroughs in doing this with advice on UDP policies for biodiversity. Planning applications should give full consideration to the effects, both direct and indirect, of development upon biodiversity, wildlife habitat and geology. Indirect effects include increased use and disturbance, hydrological changes, level of noise, pollution, shading and lighting disturbance. In Policy 3D.12, compensation is used in the context of reducing and off-setting the harm caused by development and involves the provision of features to replace those lost as a result, preferably by like with like. Most wildlife habitats are difficult to recreate, so the replacement or relocation of species and habitat should be considered only as a last resort.
	3.260 One of the key objectives of the Mayor's biodiversity strategy is to ensure that all Londoners have ready access to wildlife and natural green spaces. This is particularly important where there is a shortage of green space and in areas for regeneration. Access can be improved by making places more attractive and safer, enhancing or creating new wildlife habitats and opening up access to existing habitats. Wherever appropriate, new development should include new or enhanced habitat, or design (such as green roofs) and landscaping that promotes biodiversity, and provision for their management.

A2 BIODIVERSITY BENEFITS OF GREEN ROOFS – A SUMMARY OF RESEARCH

A2.1 Mosses/lichens

To date the only research that has been undertaken into the presence of mosses on UK green roofs was carried out in London during the winter/spring of 2004/2005. The study recorded thirty eight bryophyte species on nine roofs, with the vast majority being relatively common. However, two nationally scarce species, *Aloina ambigua* and *Thuidium abietinum spp abietinum* were also found. *Aloina ambigua* is classified as nationally scarce and its presence in London is very unusual. It was found on the roof of the Laban Dance Centre, Deptford Creek, London, and it is believed that the spores may either have been transported in the green roof substrate or colonised from the surrounding flood defences (the species is associated with mud capped walls).

A number of other species were unexpectedly discovered during the London survey. *Amblystegium serpens* is normally associated with rotting logs. Its occurrence was linked to the presence of coir netting used to hold soils in place during green roof construction. Another green roof, constructed with a volcanic growing medium held two species of moss, *Camplyopus introflexus* and *Camplyopus pyriformis* which are normally found on acid and peaty soils (Moller, 2005).

The study shows that there is a great deal of potential for mosses as an element of green roof flora.

A2.2 Plants

A study of vegetation on roofs and old wartime pillboxes in East Anglia gives an indication of which plants are suited to the harsh conditions typical of extensive green roofs (Payne, 2000). Of the 135 species of higher plant recorded in the study, one of the most common species was biting stonecrop Sedum acre, a plant widely used in generic green roof systems. Other studies that have looked at species naturally found growing on walls have recorded species such as snapdragon *Antirrhinum majus*, wallflower *Erysimum cheiri*, ivy-leaved toadflax *Cymbalaria muralis*, mercury *Mercurialis spp.*, and white dead-nettle *Lamium album*. These are also likely to occur naturally on green roofs (Grant *et al*, 2003). Ivy-leaved toadflax and white dead-nettle have been recorded on green roofs in London.

In Germany, the focus of much of the green roof research has been primarily on plant species associated with either dry meadow communities or alpine conditions; in particular, low growing grasses such as *Festuca spp.*, and species of the *Dianthus* family. Much of this research has focused on aesthetically pleasing plant species (Dunnett and Kingsbury, 2004). A number of other species have been researched for their viability as green roof plants including thymes *Thymus spp.*, *Alisons Alyssum spp.*, onion family *Allium spp.*, bell flowers *Campanula spp.* and cinquefoils *Potentilla spp.* (Kolb and Schwarz, 1999).

Figure A2.1

Dry Alpine Meadow Lucerne (courtesy M Frith)

A survey of the Moos Water Filtration Plant in Zurich, Switzerland, demonstrates well the potential for green roofs to provide habitat for rare and endangered wild plants. The five roofs were built in 1913 using local soils and cover a total area of three hactares. The site was surveyed in the early 2000s and over 175 species of higher plant were recorded, many of which classified as very rare or endangered in the Eastern Swiss Plateau region. This record included nine species of orchid, the most notable being the green-winged orchid *Orchis morio*, which was represented by over 6000 specimens. On the basis of their plant diversity the roofs have been designated a national park.

In the UK, a study at the Eden Project roof in Cornwall noted that a number plants could be seeded onto roofs with good results. These included horseshoe vetch *Hippocrepis comosa* and kidney vetch *Anthyllis vulneraria* both important food plants for a number of butterflies (Jenrick, 2005).

Research at Sheffield University is investigating the most appropriate plant mix for the moist conditions typical in the UK. The research is looking at naturalistic plantings, with both native and non-native species being considered to balance the needs of biodiversity and aesthetics (Dunnett and Kingsbury, 2004). A number of non-native plants are particularly important as forage species for a number of rare invertebrates. Included among these are Oxford ragwort *Senecio squalidus*, Canadian goldenrod *Solidago canadensis*, honesty *Lunaria annua*, michaelmas-daisies *Aster sp.*, red valerian *Centranthus ruber*, mignonette *Reseda luteola* and black horehound *Ballota nigra* (Bodsworth *et al*, 2005). A number of these have been found occurring naturally on green roofs in London, along with natives such as bird's-foot trefoil *Lotus corniculatus* and red clover *Trifolium pratense* that are also important plants for invertebrates.

A2.3 Invertebrates

Historically, much of the green roof research has focused on the performance of plants species. It has not been until relatively recently that research has looked at the fauna of green roofs. Much of this recent research has focused on invertebrates and in particular on the benefits green roofs can provide for rare species associated with brownfield land.

Figure A2.2 *Cornflower and bumble bee (courtesy Brenneisen)*

Figure A2.3 *Grasshopper Rhyl Park, Switzerland (courtesy Livingroofs.org)*

Figure A2.4 *Heath Like green roof Rhyl Park, Switzerland (courtesy Livingroofs.org)*

Research in the UK in the early 1980s and 1990s recognised the value of "post-industrial sites" for invertebrates, particularly when such sites were at the early stages of plant succession (Gilbert, 1990). Since then entomologists have studied numerous sites, discovering that many provide habitat for rare invertebrates. The shallow gravel workings and derelict land in the East Thames Corridor provide a good example. These sites have been found to support a remarkable concentration of rare invertebrates (Harvey, 2001). Many of the species found are restricted to the habitat type such as the brown banded bumble bee *Bombus humilis* and shrill carder bee *Bombus sylvarum*, which are both UK biodiversity action plan species (GLA, 2002).

In some cases brownfield sites are so rich in invertebrate populations there is serious concern that their loss through redevelopment will be detrimental to regional and national biodiversity interests. English Nature has referred to one notable site, an old oil refinery at Shellhaven, Canvey Wick, Essex, as "an English rainforest".

Swiss research in the late 1990s noted that many of the invertebrates once associated with dry river gravels and meadows along the Rhine were restricted to brownfield sites in the cities. At the same time, green roofs became a legal requirement on new buildings, and funding was approved to provide incentives to retrofit existing buildings with green roofs. The research noted that many rare and endangered invertebrate species were found on green roofs, and an even greater diversity could be encouraged by including specific features (Brenneisen, 2001).

Figure A2.5 *Basel green roof designed for rare invertebrates (courtesy Livingroofs.org)*

Figure A2.6 *Basel Green roof designed for rare invertebrates (courtesy S Wilson)*

In a study of beetles and spiders on eleven roofs in the City of Basel, 10 per cent of the beetles were listed as of nature conservation concern (Red Data Book species) and 40 per cent of recorded spiders were listed as nationally scarce (Brenneisen, 2001). Further research into wild bees and other hymenoptera (bees, wasps, ants etc) is currently being undertaken. Preliminary results show a number of species of conservation concern are commonly found using green roof systems. The research has found that naturalistic dry grassland roofs are the most productive for bees (including *Bombus humilis*) and associated species as these provide rich foraging habitat throughout the year. The majority of green roofs in Basel are not sedum based. Sedums provide a good source of nectar for wild bees but the flowering period is limited.

Research on green roof invertebrates has been undertaken in the UK since 2002. One study undertaken in London collected samples of spiders from ten green roofs and three brownfield sites. Over 3000 individual spiders were collected, representing 59 species consisting of nine per cent of the total UK and 26 per cent of the Greater London spider fauna (Kadas, 2002). Six new species were recorded for Greater London, and one new species for southern England. The survey concluded that if green roofs were to be used as mitigation for brownfield invertebrate communities, then simple proprietary sedum based systems were not appropriate (Kadas, 2002; Gedge and Kadas, 2005).

A further study commissioned by English Nature in 2002 surveyed eight green roofs in London. A total of 136 invertebrate species were recorded, including a number of unusual and uncommon species associated with harsh and dry habitat conditions, Some had not previously been recorded in the London area (Table A2.1). The study concluded that although the current conventional green roof systems that are being used in the London area, such as sedum mats, support interesting invertebrate fauna, such roofs do not necessarily provide refuge for the rare species associated with brownfield sites (Jones, 2002).

Table A2.1 *Unusual and uncommon species of invertebrate found on green roofs in London (Jones, 2002)*

Species	Status	Habitat preference
Anticus angustatus	Nationally scarce	Sandy shores/salt marshes
Tachys parvulus	Nationally scarce	Gravel pits and shingle
Olibrus flavicornis	Nationally rare	
Oxypoda lurida	Nationally scarce	Gravel pits and shingle
Chlamydatus evanescens	Nationally rare	Coastal
Erigone alestris	Very local	
Pardosa agrestis	Nationally scarce	Chalk clay pits and undercliff

A long-term study is currently being carried out at Royal Holloway College, University of London. This is investigating a number of the green roofs and brownfield sites studied in the previous English Nature surveys. At present over 254 species of invertebrates have been recorded (Table A2.2).

Table A2.2 *Invertebrates found on green roof and brownfield habitats*

Invertebrate group	No of species	National status	Scarce or rare locally
Arachnids	73	6	8
Coleoptera	125	6	22
Hymenoptera	38	3	2
Hemiptera	13	1	2
Diptera	3		
Orthoptera	2		
	254	16	34

Several species of national status recorded in the Royal Holloway study were also recorded in previous studies both in Switzerland and the UK. These included:

- *Tachys parvulus* – found in all three London studies and in Basel, Switzerland
- *Zodarion ithalicum* – identified as a species likely to benefit from green roofs in the English Nature report (Jones, 2002), and found to be relatively common on roofs studied in Switzerland
- *Palustris agresti* – a nationally scarce species of spider, usually associated with chalk clay pits and undercliffs, was recorded in all the studies
- *Chlamydatus evanescens* – a rare plant bug recorded in both the English Nature and Royal Holloway College studies as present on green roofs
- *Zodarion ithalicum* – identified as a species likely to benefit from green roofs in the English Nature report (Jones, 2002) and one that was found to be relatively common on roofs studied in Switzerland.

The Swiss and UK studies discussed have highlighted a number of key principles which should be followed when trying to attract a rich diversity of invertebrates to green roofs (Kadas, 2002; Jones, 2002; Brenneisen, 2004). These include:

- use a variety of substrate types
- use a variety of substrate depths allowing for bare areas of soil and gravels
- use a variety of plant structures from low to dense vegetation
- use local wildflowers seeds associated with dry grasslands.

Although sedum based systems have intrinsic interest for invertebrates, including a few species that are considered rare or of importance, the research highlights that the greatest benefits for invertebrate biodiversity are achieved through the use of more naturalistic green roof systems.

A2.4 Birds

The English Nature report (Grant *et al*, 2003) highlights the potential of green roofs for nine bird species listed in the National, London and Birmingham biodiversity action plans, and the biodiversity audits for London and East Anglia. These are kestrel *Falco tinnunculus*, swallow *Hirundo rustica*, house martin *Delichon urbica*, pied wagtail *Motacilla alba*, black redstart *Phoenicurus ochruros*, song thrush *Turdus philomelos*, house sparrow *Passer domesticus*, goldfinch *Carduelis carduelis* and greenfinch *Carduelis chloris*.

A short study of a number green roofs in Sussex in 2004 and 2005 noted the presence of a number of notable bird species (Table A2.3).

Table A2.3 *Notable bird species recorded on green roofs in Sussex (Burgess, 2004)*

Species	Activity
Ringed Plover *Charadrius hiaticula*	Possibly breeding
Little Ringed Plover *Charadrius dubius*	Possibly breeding
Skylark *Alauda arvensis*	Breeding
Song Thrush *Turdus philomelos*	Foraging
Starling *Sturnus vulgaris*	Foraging
Linnet *Carduelis cannabina*	Foraging

The presence of breeding skylarks, and possible breeding ringed and little ringed plover, was noted on the roof of the Rolls Royce Factory, Sussex; the largest green roof in the UK at 40 000 m^2. These results are in keeping with evidence from the continent where all three species have been recorded breeding on large green roofs. Other species seen breeding on green roofs in northern Europe are oystercatcher *Haematopus ostralegus*, lapwing *Vanellus vanellus* and common tern *Sterna hirundo* (Brenneisen, 2001). Research is currently being undertaken in Switzerland into ways of improving green roof habitat for lapwing and little ringed plover.

Figure A2.7 *Pipes to provide protection for ground nesting bird chicks (courtesy livingroofs.org)*

A study of green roofs in Switzerland in 2000 recorded 25 species of birds, and grouped them into three categories relating to the frequency at which they used roofs for nesting (Table A2.4).

Table A2.4 *Birds and frequency of use on green roofs in Basel (Brenneisen, 2001)*

High frequency	Medium frequency	Low frequency
Feral pigeon	Collared dove	Grey wagtail
White wagtail	Carrion crow	Wheatear
Black redstart	Magpie	Whinchat
House sparrow	Tree sparrow	
	Goldfinch	

The Swiss study arrived at two important conclusions:

1. Within the survey area, urban roofs appeared to be used more frequently by birds than roofs in suburban and rural locations.
2. Height and aspect of the roofs appeared to have no effect on the type of species or the frequency of use (Brenneisen, 2001).

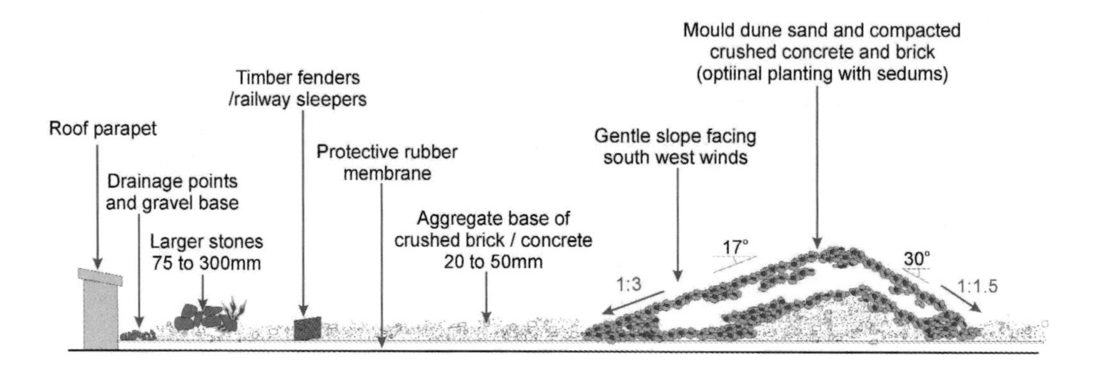

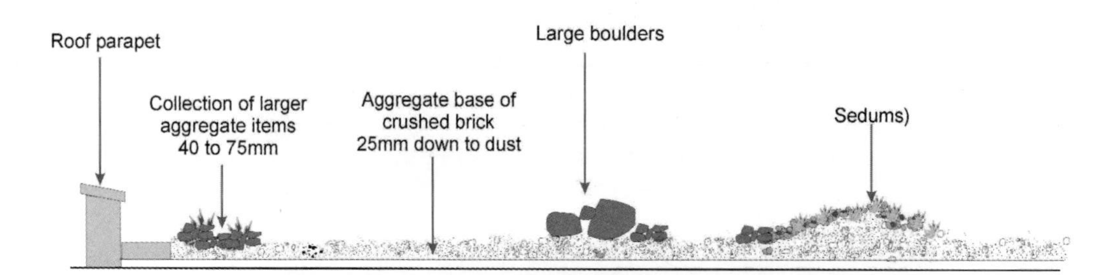

Figure A2.8 *Cross-section of green roof design for black redstarts (courtesy Livingroofs.org)*

The available evidence suggests that there is great potential for green roofs to provide benefits for bird species. Generic systems in urban situations are likely to provide habitat for more common species, whereas roofs specifically designed to mimic habitats within the urban fabric, such as brownfield sites, are likely to be more successful for important species such as black redstart *Phoenicurus ochruros*. The potential of large green roofs for ground nesting birds is evident from the few UK and European studies carried out to date.

Examples of specific green roof designs for birds are shown in Figures A2.7 and A2.8.

A3 THE CONTRIBUTION OF GREEN ROOFS TO STORMWATER MANAGEMENT

1 Extensive green roof (70 mm depth), Philadelphia
Reference *Vegetated rood cover, Philadelphia, Pennsylvania (United States Environmental Protection Agency, 2000)*
Location Philadelphia, USA
Design/construction The roof was designed to detain a 24 hour duration rainfall event with an annual probability of 50 % (one in two years) **Note:** The duration and probability refer to local conditions in Philadelphia, USA, not UK rainfall events The extensive roof cover had an overall thickness of 70 mm. The growth medium used had a saturated moisture content of 45 % and the saturated infiltration capacity was 89 mm/h
Volume reduction Monitoring of a trial section found that negligible runoff occurred from rainfall events less than 15 mm depth
Peak flow reduction The most intense storm occurred after the roof was already saturated by a previous extended period of rainfall. However, attenuation was still significant (Figure A3.1). This suggests that even when retention is no longer occurring the effects of vegetation on the surface and the infiltration capacity of the substrate will still slow down the rate of runoff from the roof
Other information

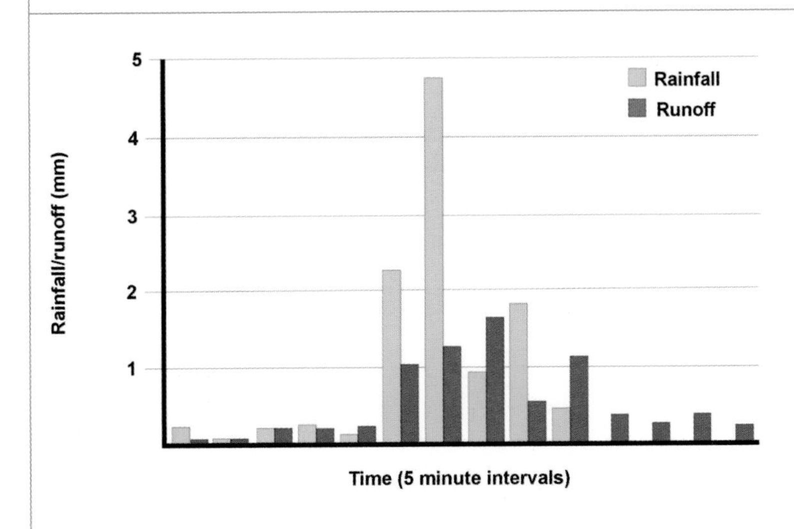

Figure A3.1 *Runoff attenuation for trial roof in Philadelphia (USEPA, 2000)*

2 Extensive green roofs (75 mm and 100 mm depths), Toronto
Reference Performance evaluation of an extensive green roof, (Lui and Minor, 2005)
Location Toronto, Canada
Design/construction Three roofs were monitored, two green roofs with substrate depths of 75 mm and 100 mm and a non-vegetated roof of standard design to act as a control. The two green roofs were constructed on a 460 m^2 roof that was divided into two. The area of the control roof was 100 m^2. Green roof North G comprises a composite semi-rigid plastic drainage and filter mat and a 100 mm thick substrate (lightweight growing medium). Green roof South S comprises expanded polystyrene drainage panels and a geotextile filter fabric. It has 75 mm of lightweight porous ceramic granular substrate. **Note:** The vegetation was not fully established during monitoring period. Retention efficiency depends on the intensity and the duration of rainfall and extent of previous wetting (known as antecedent conditions)
Volume reduction An average annual reduction in runoff 57 % was measured from both green roofs (ie the green roofs had 43 % of the runoff of the control roof) There was 100 % reduction on both green roofs (ie 0 % runoff) in summer for all events with less than 15 mm rainfall after six days of dry weather It was found that the roof with the thinner substrate was less effective at reducing the volume of runoff. Periodically it became saturated and gave same runoff volume as control roof
Peak flow reduction Flow rates from both the green roofs were significantly reduced in all seasons A lag time of 20 to 40 min in summer was measured and peak flow reduction of 25 to 60 % was achieved from both roofs In autumn, a shorter lag times was measured. When the green roofs became saturated the lag time was the same as the control, but a peak flow reduction of 10 to 30 % was measured
Other information

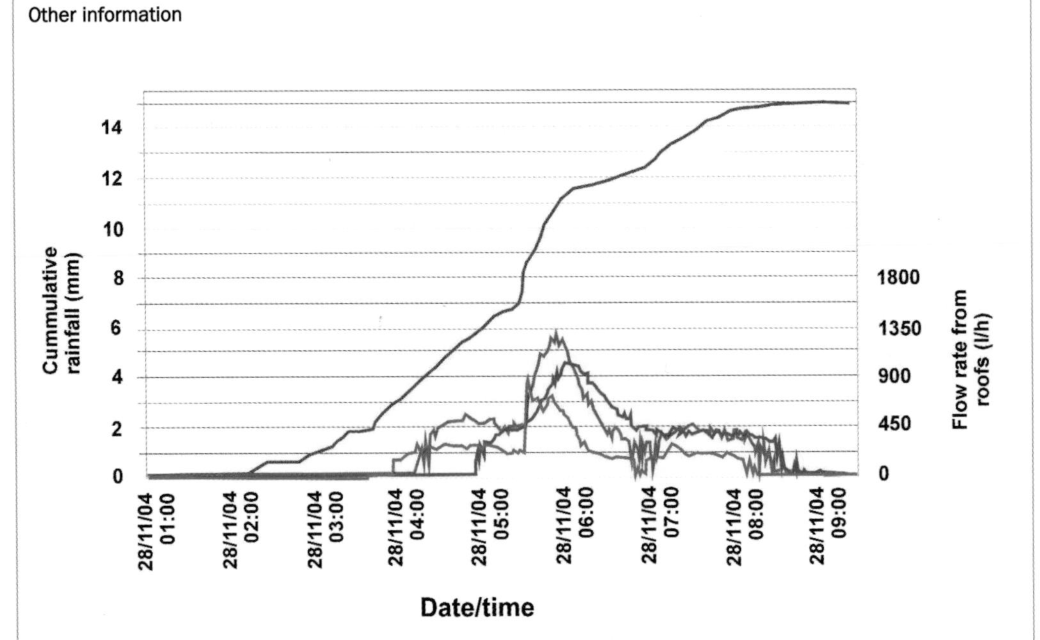

Figure A3.2 *Response of green roofs to 15 mm rainfall following seven days of multiple small rain events (Trends from data by Karen Lui and John Minor, 2005)*

3	Summary of Swedish research on green roofs, various roofs

Reference

Lundberg (2005)

Location

Sweden

Design/construction

N/A

Volume reduction

Reports that research has demonstrated that average annual runoff from extensive green roof is about 50 % (no further details are provided)

Peak flow reduction

N/A

Other information

This is a general summary of research in Sweden. Other important points are that it found that the most important factor in reducing runoff is thickness of substrate

It also found that mosses are very effective at delaying rainfall runoff

4 Extensive green roofs (75 mm and 100 mm depth), North Carolina
Reference *Hydrologic and water quality performance from green roofs in Goldsboro and Raleigh (Moran et al, 2005)*
Location North Carolina, USA
Design/construction Two trial green roofs were monitored over several months i The first had 75 mm substrate depth. ii The second had 100 mm substrate depth and a 7 % slope. The first roof (i) was monitored from April 2003 to September 2004 and the second roof (ii) was monitored from July 2004 to September 2004 The substrate used for both roofs was 55 % expanded slate, 30 % sand and 15 % compost
Volume reduction i The first roof gave an average retention of 63 % (37 % runoff) ii The second, deeper roof gave a 55 % average retention (45 % runoff) The performance of the roofs was found to vary with rainfall patterns. Lower retention (higher runoff) was recorded for higher intensity events and for numerous events with short dry periods between
Peak flow reduction i There was an 87 per cent average reduction in peak flow rate measured for the first roof for an average peak rainfall of 36 mm/h. A lag time of at least 30 mins in 60 per cent of events was recorded. In some cases a lag time of up to 4hours was measured ii Peak flow reductions observed at the first green roof for rain events larger than 38 mm averaged 51 per cent. The amount of reduction increased for smaller storm events. This is due to the fact that larger storms tended to have high runoff intensities reaching more than 76 mm/hr iii The second roof gave a 57 per cent average reduction in peak flow rate for average peak rainfall of 44mm/h

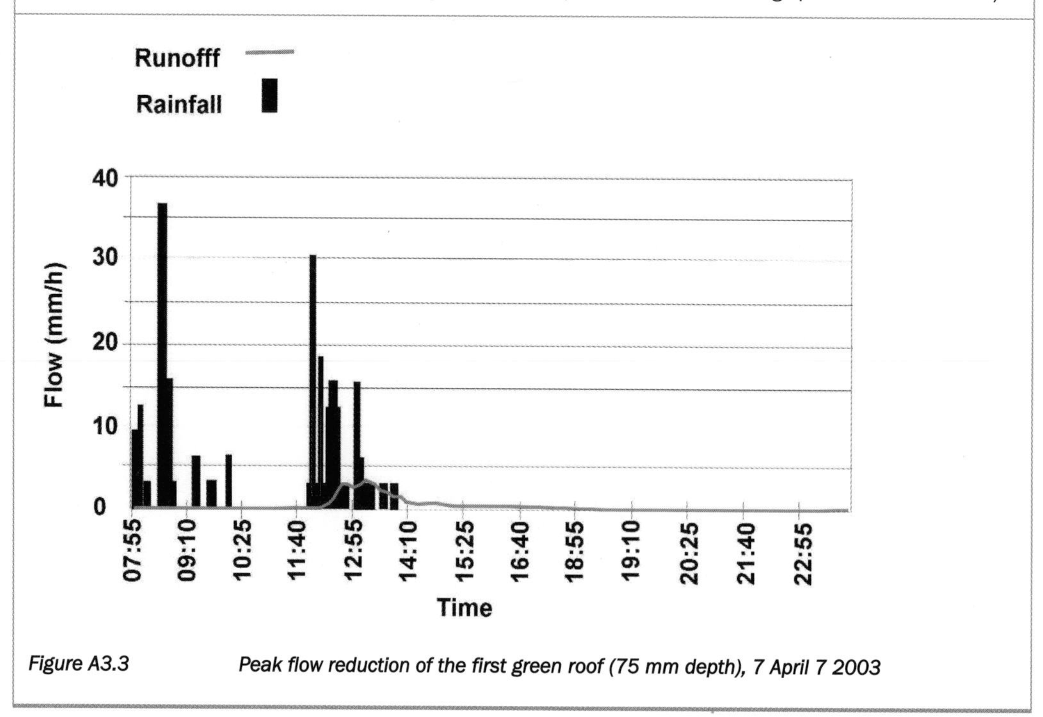

Figure A3.3 ***Peak flow reduction of the first green roof (75 mm depth), 7 April 7 2003***

5	Extensive green roof (100–120 mm depth) Portland – research by the City of Portland
Reference *Data taken from a summary in Moran et al (2005)*	
Location Portland, USA	
Design/construction An extensive green roof with 100 to 120 mm substrate depth was monitored over 15 months in 2002/03.	
Volume reduction An average retention 69 % (31 % runoff) was found.	
Peak flow reduction Peak flow reduction of 80 % was recorded.	

6	Extensive green roof (127 mm depth), Michigan – research by University of Michigan
Reference *Data taken from a summary in Moran et al (2005)*	
Location Michigan, USA	
Design/construction An extensive green roof with 127 mm substrate depth was monitored over twenty-four rainfall events.	
Volume reduction An average volume retention of 66 % (34 % runoff) was measured	
Peak flow reduction It was found that the peak flow rate was reduced and total runoff was delayed from green roofs when compared to normal roofs	
Other information This study also found that thicker substrate depths and shallower slopes gave better volume reduction of runoff 60 mm thick substrate, 6.5 % slope, 28 % runoff 40 mm thick substrate, 6.5 % slope, 31 % runoff 40 mm thick substrate, 2 % slope, 26 % runoff	

7	**Effect of orientation on the water balance of green roofs, various roofs in Europe** **Mentens *et al* (2003)**

Location

Various locations in Europe

Design/construction

The paper is a discussion of the analysis of data from a wide literature review and comprehensive details of the construction are not included

Volume reduction

An example of estimated annual runoff rates for roofs in Brussels is given (calculated using the runoff equation below):

Standard roof 81 %

Standard roof with 50 mm gravel 77 %

Green roof 50 mm 50 %

Green roof 100 mm 45 %

Green roof 150 mm 40 %

Peak flow reduction

N/A

Other information

The study looked at 628 records from 18 papers mainly in Germany.

A runoff equation was derived from the results:

Annual runoff in mm = 693 – (1.15 × annual rainfall) + (0.001 × annual rainfall2) – 8 × substrate thickness

Annual rainfall in mm/yr and substrate thickness in cm. Valid for average annual rainfall between 554 mm and 1347 mm and substrates between 30 mm and 380 mm thickness.

8	**Extensive green roof (140 mm depth), Toronto**

Reference

York University rooftop garden stormwater quantity and quality performance monitoring report (MacMillan, 2003)

Location

Toronto, Canada

Design/construction

A green roof with 140 mm substrate depth at 10 % slope was monitored.

Volume reduction

It was found that the green roof reduced annual runoff by 55 %

Peak flow reduction

Peak flow rates were as follows:

10–19 mm storm – 85 % reduction

20–29 mm storm – 82 % reduction

30–39 mm storm – 68 % reduction

>40 mm storm – 46 % reduction

Other information

It was found that runoff increased as the roof became saturated. The research concluded that antecedent conditions significantly affect performance of the roof in stormwater management.

9 Extensive green roof (depth 150 mm), Ottowa
Reference *NRC's Institute for research in construction studying plant survivability and stormwater management in Ottowa (Lui and Boivin, 2002)*
Location Ottowa, Canada
Design/construction An extensive green roof with substrate depth of 150 mm was monitored for one rainfall event over a 15 hour period in October 2001
Volume reduction 76 % runoff was recorded (but roof was already wet)
Peak flow reduction Rainfall intensity of 1.8 mm/h gave a runoff rate of 0.8 mm/h (although this increased as roof became saturated)
Other information A lag time of 35 min was also recorded

10 Green roof, 350 mm depth, New York
Reference *Vancouver Public Library green roof monitoring project (Johnston et al, 2003)*
Location New York, USA
Design/construction A green roof with 350 mm of light weight substrate comprising 33.3 % washed sand, 33.3 % pumice and 33.3 % compost was monitored in order to calibrate a stormwater drainage computer program used in the USA
Volume reduction A 48 % reduction in annual runoff was recorded
Peak flow reduction Peak flow reductions were as follows: > 80 % in summer small events 30 % in winter small events < 5 % in large events

Other information

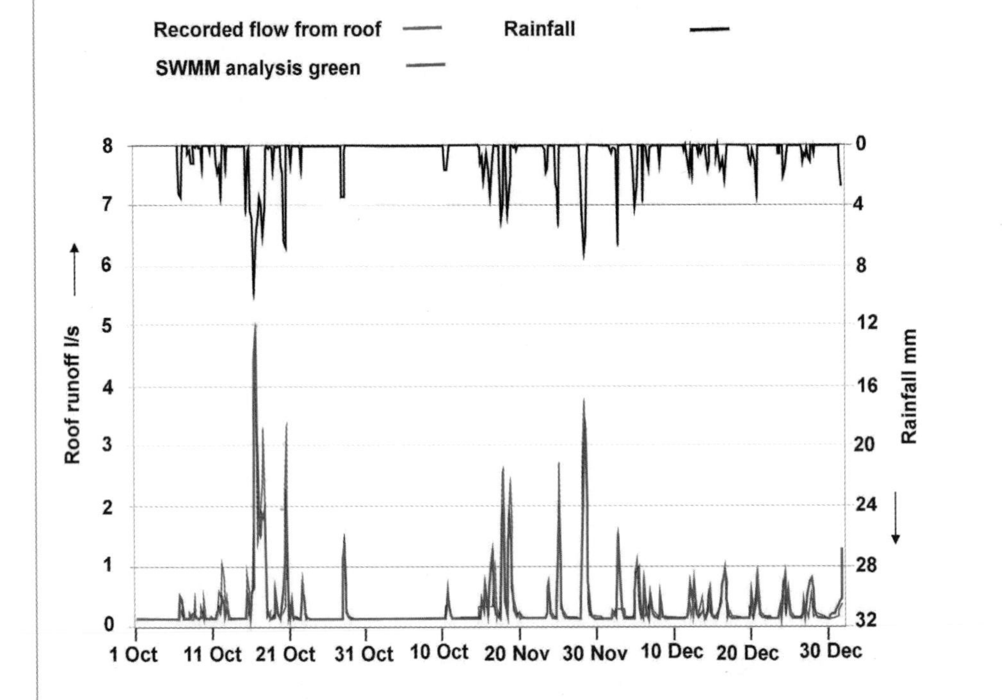

Figure A3.4 *Green roof runoff model calibration (general trends from Johnston et al 2003)*

Developed a stormwater drainage model using SWMM (a computer program used for drainage design in the USA) and calibrated it to the green roof monitoring (see Figure A3.4)

11 Test cells with different types of vegetation, Sheffield
Reference *Vegetation composition and structure significantly influence green roof performance (Dunnett et al, 2005)*
Location Sheffield, UK
Design/construction Test cells measuring 0.6 m by 0.6 m were planted with different types of vegetation. A natural soil substrate was used and the runoff was monitored over three years (1997 to 2000)
Volume reduction The reduction in volume of the total annual runoff was estimated to be 40–45 %, depending on vegetation type
Peak flow reduction N/A

12 Extensive sedum roofs – various manufacturers, Chicago
Reference *City of Chicago roof test plot study: Stormwater and temperature results (LaBerge et al, 2005)*
Location Chicago, USA
Design/construction Extensive sedum roofs from various manufacturers were monitored. There was a two per cent slope on roofs to the channel collector drain **Note:** The thickness of the substrate is not known Nine sheds of 3.3 m² roof area were monitored for two years. Continuous monitoring was carried out between May and October in 2003 and in 2004
Volume reduction The runoff measured from the sedum roofs were as follows **Note:** All figures are quoted as percentage of runoff from the control roof For storms less than 8 mm, 10 % runoff was measured For storms >23 mm 21 to 37 % runoff was measured A rainfall event of 25 mm over 6 to 12 h gave 70–80 % runoff Individual or consecutive cumulative storms < 23 mm gave 0–24 % runoff (mean 6 %) Individual or consecutive cumulative storms > 23 mm gave 5–95 % runoff (mean 57 %)

A4 GREEN ROOFS AND POLLUTION REMOVAL FROM STORMWATER – A SUMMARY OF RESEARCH

The ability of green roofs to improve the quality of runoff has been found to be variable. The following sections summarise the finding of a number of studies that monitored the pollutants in rainwater and green roof runoff.

A4.1 Swedish Research on green roofs and information outreach (Lundberg, 2005)

A summary of research in Sweden (Lundberg, 2005) reports on the monitoring of green roofs where filtration through the green roof plots was found to remove nitrogen from the runoff. However, it was found to increase the concentrations of phosphorous and potassium. There was little effect on heavy metal concentrations in the runoff.

A4.2 Study of extensive "green roofs" in Berlin (Kohler and Schmidt, 2003)

Kohler and Schmidt (2003) monitored experimental green roof plots at the Technical University of Berlin for three years. The roofs were constructed using a recycled soil substrate of loamy sand with rock fragments. The results demonstrated that the nature of the substrate, the organic matter content and the establishment of vegetation all affect pollution removal rates. Conversely, these three factors also affect the rate at which nutrients are leached from the substrate.

The retention of pollutants was found to be good for both metals and nutrients. Phosphate retention increased with time as the vegetation became more established, as shown on Figure A4.1. However, it was noted that the substrate could add pollutants to runoff immediately after installation.

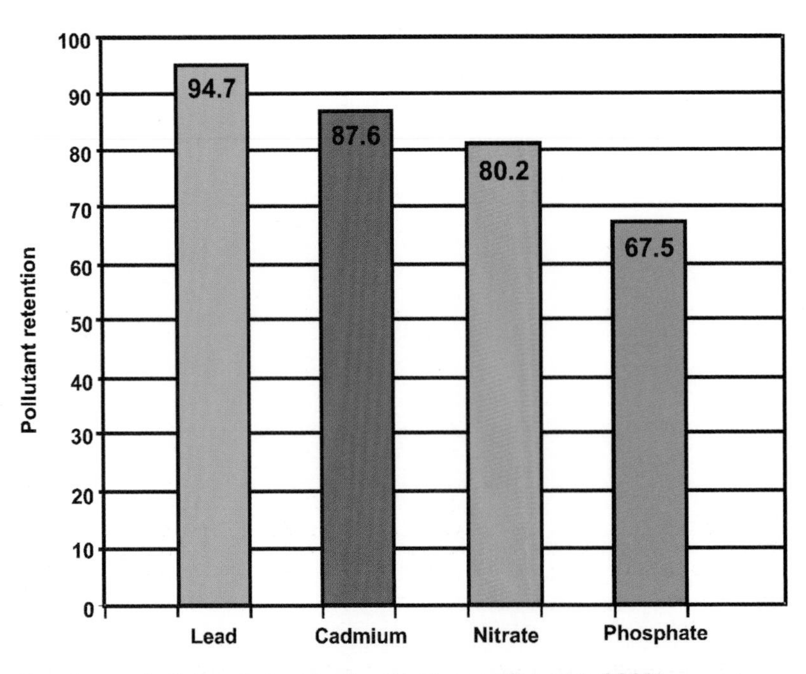

Figure A4.1 *Development of phosphate retention (Kohler and Schmidt, 2003)*

Kohler and Schmidt (2003) also discuss a study on the quality of runoff from a green roof on a development at Potsdamer Platz in Berlin, Germany. Trials were carried out with different commercially available substrates, based on lava rocks, expanded slate, and a sand/lava/pumice mix. The results indicated that all the substrates gave an increase in inorganic contaminants in the runoff.

Each different substrate was placed on a 2 m^2 test plot. The electrical conductivity of the runoff was measured (the higher the value the greater the pollution by inorganic contaminants). The results are shown in Figure A4.2. Rainfall usually has a conductivity of between 10 µS/cm and 100 µS/cm. Runoff from all the different substrates showed an increase in conductivity and a rise in pH from about 6.3 in the rainfall up to around 7.5 in the runoff from the green roofs. The turbidity of the runoff from the roofs decreased over time. (Figure A4.3).

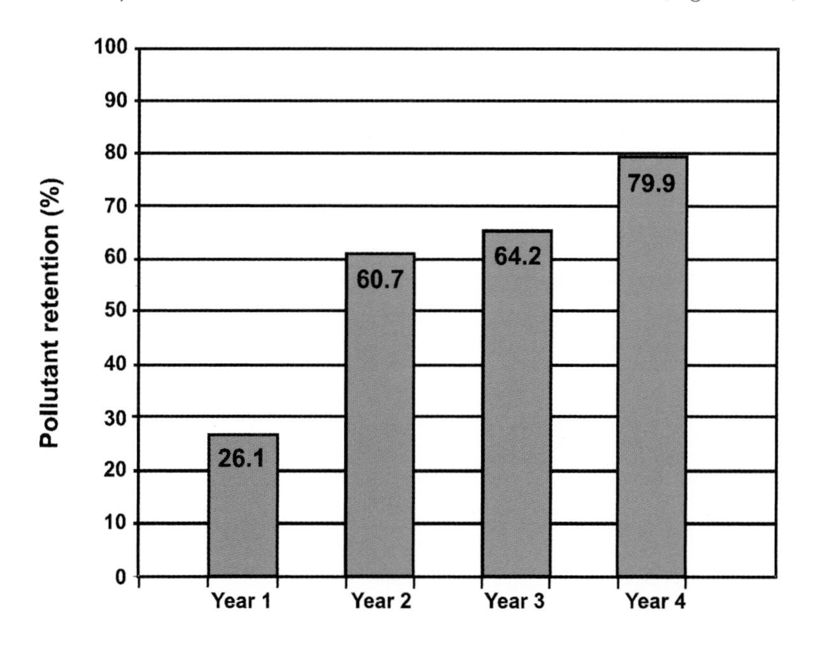

Figure A4.2 *Electrical conductivity of runoff between 8/7/97 and 1/21/98 (Kohler and Schmidt 2003)*

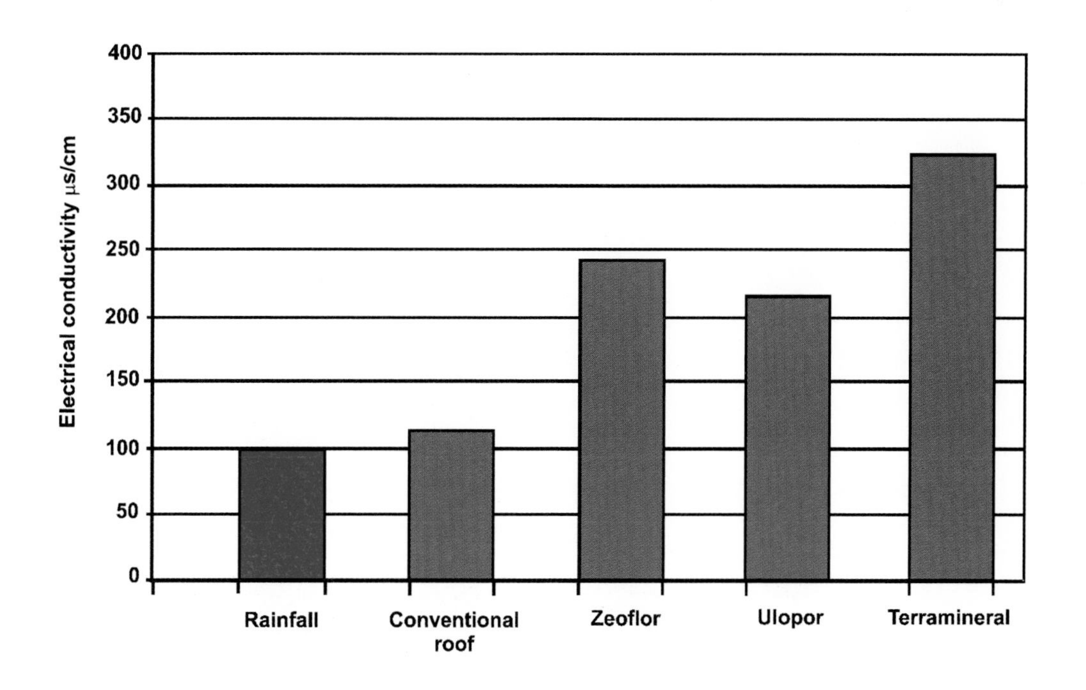

Figure A4.3 *Change in turbidity of runoff, measured at 420 mm 1/8/98 to 21/1/98 (Kohler and Schmidt 2003)*

The roofs showed a reduction in nitrogen (total discharge from green roofs of between 10 and 80 mg/m^3 during the monitoring period) and phosphate was also removed from the runoff (total discharge of between 75 and 100 mg/m^3). The total discharge of nitrogen and phosphate from the conventional roof was 265 mg/m^3 and 145 mg/m^3 respectively.

A4.3 York University rooftop garden stormwater quantity and quality performance monitoring report, (Macmillan, 2003)

Variable performance of green roofs for pollutant removal was found in a study by Macmillan (2003), who reported that green roofs increased the loadings of most metals, cations, anions and several nutrients. They did, however, reduce the loadings of total suspended solids, nitrogen complexes, biochemical oxygen demand and polynuclear aromatic hydrocarbons in the runoff.

A5 GREEN ROOFS FOR CLIMATE CHANGE ADAPTATION AND MITIGATION – FURTHER CASE STUDIES

A5.1 Case study – evapotranspiration measurement of green roofs (Kolb, 2002)

The evapotranspiration rates from a number of green roofs in Germany were measured and as expected, the evapotranspiration rate of intensive green roofs was found to be generally higher than that of an extensive roof. In winter both types of roof had a low rate of evapotranspiration due to climatic factors.

With average monthly rainfall of 47 mm, the evapotranspiration rate for the model extensive green roof was 21 mm or 45 per cent during the year. From May until August almost all the recorded rainfall evaporates from the roofs, in November, December and January there were only insignificant evapotranspiration levels.

An average runoff of 364 mm which is the equivalent of an evapotranspiration rate of 68 per cent was measured for intensive green roof with a substrate depth of 300 mm and lawn vegetation.

A5.2 Case study – green roof surface temperature

Measurements of green roof surface temperature were carried out on an experimental green roof, located at Neubrandenburg University, Neubrandenburg, Germany (Koehler, 2005). The roof is shown in Figure A5.1. The roof has areas of different substrate. The section of the roof on the left hand side of Figure A5.1 has a crushed fired clay based substrate and is well vegetated. The section of the roof to the right hand side of Figure A5.1 has a darker blown slate substrate and is less well vegetated.

Figure A5.1 *An experimental green roof at the Green Roof Centre, Neubrandenburg University*

Figure A5.3 is a thermographic image of the roof and demonstrates the effect of the green roof on its microclimate. The hotter areas (red and purple) indicate where there are patches of bare substrate. The cooler areas (yellow and green) show where the vegetation is located. There are three temperature cross-sections through the image (Figure A5.4). Section L01 is mainly vegetation, L02 mainly darker blown slate substrate and L03 is the concrete block roof perimeter path.

Figure A5.2

The experimental roof in May 2003 before the vegetation was fully established. The two substrate types can be clearly seen (courtesy P Early)

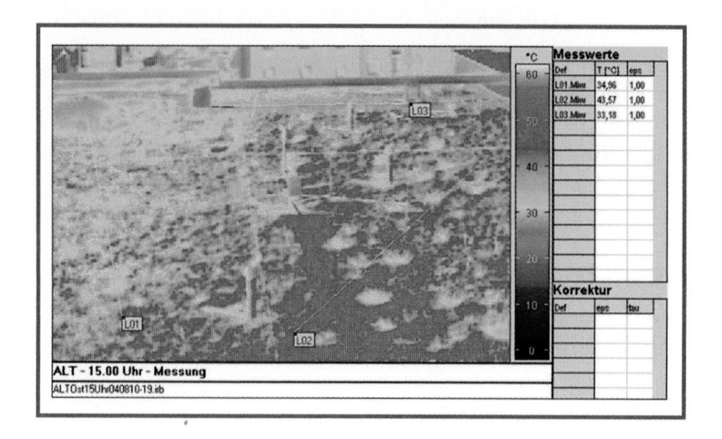

Figure A5.3 *A picture of a green roof taken with a thermographic camera at 15:00 on a hot summers day in August 2004 (Koehler, 2005)*

Figure A5.4 shows that the areas of bare substrate are hotter than the areas of vegetation by a substantial margin. The substrate temperature is typically between 40°C and 50°C with a mean temperature of 43.57°C, while the vegetation is typically between 30°C and 40°C with a mean temperature of 34.96°C.

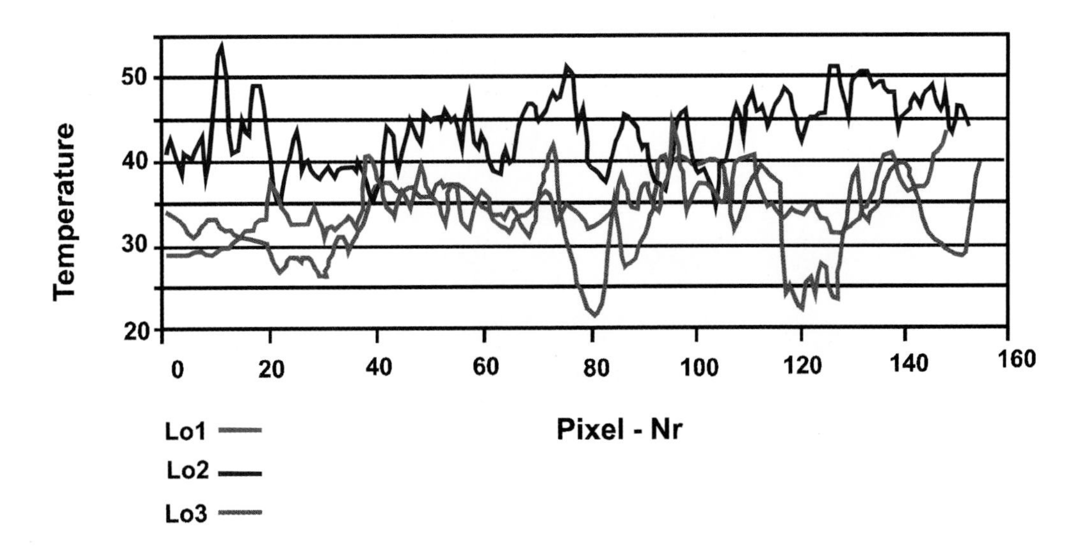

Figure A5.4 *Temperature cross-sections through the thermographic image (Koehler, 2005)*

Other interesting observations from this experiment are:

- the concrete block perimeter path stores thermal energy throughout the day, starting at the lowest temperature of all three cross-sections in the morning, the path warms up to become the hottest cross-section by the evening
- the lightweight blown slate does not have a large thermal mass, and so heats up rapidly when the sun shines on it. It is also the coolest cross-section in the middle of the night
- the cross-section through the vegetation remains close to the local air temperature.

Throughout the day, significantly less energy is converted to heat by the vegetation than by the dark blown slate substrate.

This study demonstrates that green roofs are much cooler than bare roofs in the summer. This could have an impact on reducing the urban heat island effect.

A5.3 Case study – measurement of energy balance (Koehler and Schmidt, 2002)

The energy balance of green roofs has been investigated at Neubrandenburg University, Berlin (Koehler and Schmidt, 2002).

The energy inputs and outputs for a green roof and a bitumen control roof were calculated for the summer months of June to August 2000. The calculations were made using the daily mean measurements of global radiation, radiation inputs and outputs, surface temperature, precipitation and the roof runoff (Figure A5.5).

Figure A5.5
Measuring station on the a green roof of Ufa Fabrik, Berlin (courtesy P Early)

The albedo of the bitumen control roof was 0.09 and the albedo for the test green roof was 0.15. In the period 4 June 2000 to 31 August 2000 the precipitation level was 185.4 mm plus 16 mm wetting loss. These 16 mm were equated with the evaporative loss of the bitumen roofs. In the same period the runoff from the green roof was 46.4 mm.

A detailed analysis of the energy balance of the two roofs is shown in Figures A5.6 and A5.7. These figures show the results of energy measurement for the experimental period.

For the experiment period, 1185 Wh of energy received by the green roof was converted into evaporative cooling and 803 Wh reflected. This compares with just 123 Wh and 429 Wh respectively for the bitumen roof. As a result of the increased surface temperature of the bitumen roof there was an additional 428 Wh of long-wave radiation emitted from the bitumen roof.

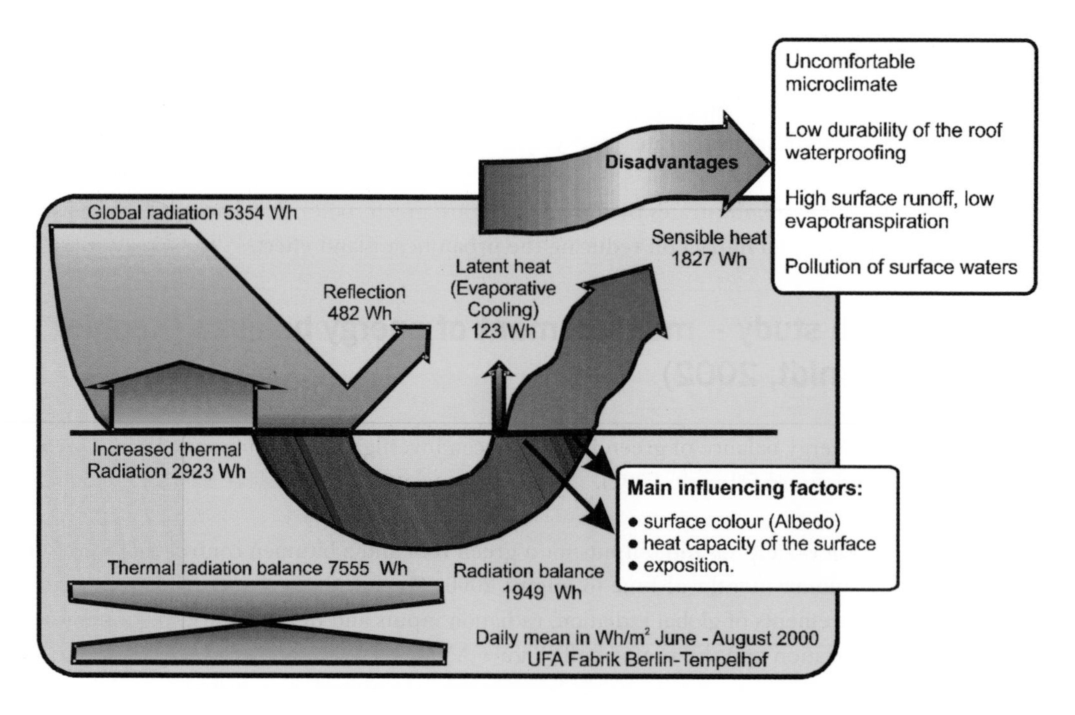

Figure A5.6 *Gross energy balance for the bitumen roof, daily mean (courtesy Marco Schmidt)*

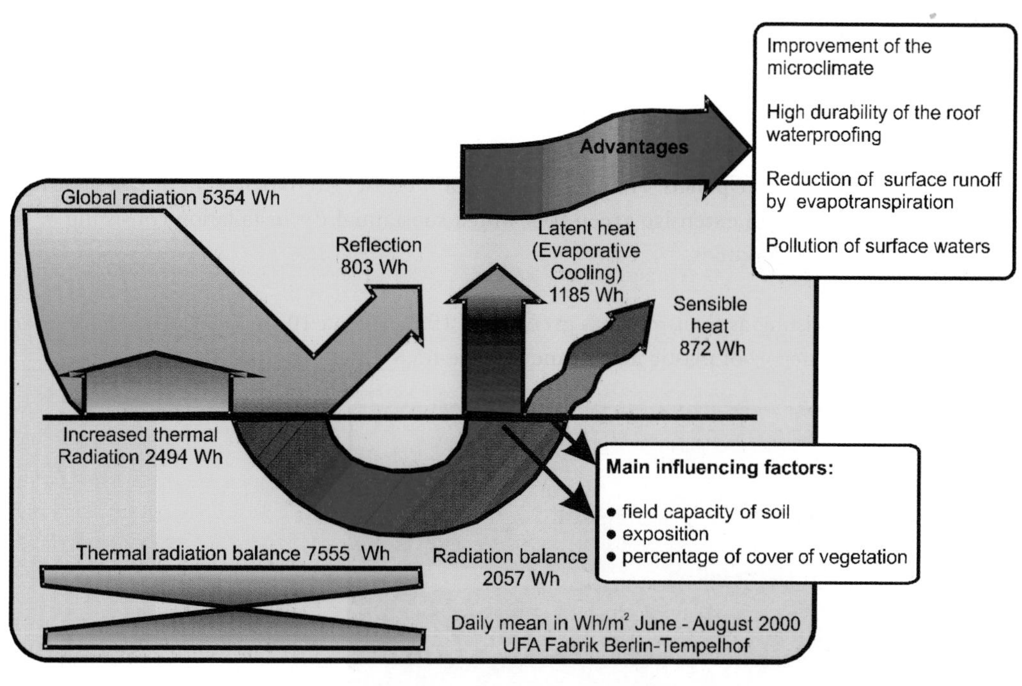

Figure A5.7 *Gross energy balance for the green roof (courtesy Marco Schmidt)*

Precipitation during the summer of 2000 was 202 mm, the exact equivalent of the long-term annual mean. But in the summer 2001 there was considerably less rainfall (72 mm) and the evaporative cooling was significantly lower (546 kWh/m^2). The trials demonstrated that ground level natural landscapes are much more effective coolers than green roofs as there is a lot more groundwater available for evapotranspiration.

Between 1987 and 1989 trial plots studied by Koehler and Schmidt showed evaporative cooling values of 356 kWh/m^2, 298 kWh/m^2 and 256 kWh/m^2 respectively. The mean evaporative cooling was 303 kWh/m^2 for the duration of the three year experiment. Hence, these trial plots used on average 1.09*109 joules/m^2 of energy per year with an average annual evapotranspiration of available rainfall of 445 mm. If the specific heat capacity of the air is fixed at 0.0013 J/(cm$^{3\circ}$C), one greened square metre of roof can cool down 1.6 m^3 of air by 1°C in one minute. The equivalent cost for the electrical energy for 303 kWh/m^2 of cooling per year is more than the one-off investment for the green roof.

Further measurements were carried out at "Ufa-Fabrik" in Berlin, on 20 June 2001, which was a day with a high rate of solar radiation. Three days beforehand there was rainfall of 5.5 mm so the green roof had been watered.

The surface of the bitumen roof showed a temperature fluctuation during the day from 5°C at 4am to 56°C at 1pm, which is a difference of 51°C. The temperatures recorded on the green roof were between 7.7°C and 30.7°C, which is temperature difference of less than half that for the bitumen roof. The sealing layer under the green roof showed a temperature difference of only 10°C during the day. During the month of July 2001 the mean daily temperature range on the bitumen roof was between 14.5°C and 46.5°C, a difference of 32°C. In contrast, the mean daily temperature range on the green roof was between 19.3 and 25.3°C, a difference of 6°C.

So from the experiments carried out at × (or × and ×) it can be seen that:

- the process of evapotranspiration and a higher albedo keeps the surface of the green roof much cooler than an equivalent bitumen roof
- diurnal temperature fluctuations are lower than for a typical bitumen roof
- the cooler green roof transfers less heat into the local microclimate. This may have some effect in reducing the urban heat island effect.

A5.4 Case study – hybrid green roof with PV (Koehler and Schmidt, 2002a)

In the first instance it may seem that a green roof precludes the use of elements such as roof-mounted solar panels. However, this is not the case. An experiment at Ufa-Fabrik, Berlin, monitored an extensive green roof with a substantial PV installation consisting of both tracked and fixed modules.

The existing asphalt roof was greened in 1992 using a 10 cm layer of soil and vermiculite on a new waterproof plastic membrane (Figure A5.8).

Figure A5.8
Roof membrane and vermiculite

Monitoring of the green roof began in 1992. The PV panels were installed on the southern half of the roof in 1998-1999 (Figure A5.10). The northern half of the existing green roof was left as a control roof (ie does not have PV-panels) (Figure A5.9).

Figure A5.9
Northern green "control roof" of Ufa-Fabrik, Berlin, May 2003

Figure A5.10

Southern experimental green roof with PV panels at Ufa-Fabrik, Berlin, May 2003

A total of 400 m² of PV arrays were placed on the green roof with a peak capacity of 53 kWatts and an annual production of 37 000 kWh (equivalent to 33 tons CO_2 emissions if the average European electricity generating mix is used). The roof was allowed to seed itself through natural colonisation.

Table A5.1 ***Results of covering green roof with PV-panels (Ufa-Fabrik, Berlin) (Koehler and Schmidt et al, 2002)***

Description	1992-99 Before PV-panel installation	2001 Northern part of roof without PV-panels	2001 Southern part of roof with PV-panels
Average number of plant species	41	41	43
Average cover of all higher plant species (%)	89	85	97
Maximum height of plants (cm)	65	110	118
Average height of plant species (cm)	22	15	38
Average cover of genus "sedum" (%)	-	48	27
Number of plant species benefited by shade of PV-panels	-	-	7

The introduction of the PV panels altered the roof microclimate by introducing shading elements. The level of shade was dependent on the location of the PV-panel and whether it remained stationary or not. The creation of shading by the introduction of the PV panels, resulted in an increase in the number of plant species found on the roof. The average plant height also increased.

As sunlight shines on a PV-panel, it warms up and the electrical characteristics of the panel change. When there is an irradiance of 1000 W/m² shining directly on a panel, typically it is found that the panel will be approximately 30°C warmer than the surrounding air. This leads to a reduction in the open circuit voltage and a slight increase of short circuit current, which leads to a lower solar radiation to electricity conversion efficiency. For mono and multi-crystalline PV-panels the increased temperature will result in a reduction in conversion efficiency of 0.4–0.5 %/°C (Krauter and Ochs, 2003). The introduction of a green roof cools the PV-panels because of the evapotranspiration from the vegetative layer, thereby maintaining higher electricity production than would otherwise be the case.

A5.5 Case study – embodied energy and greenhouse effect of roof construction (Ernst, 2003)

A desktop study of the environmental impact of different recommended flat roof construction types, has been carried out using standard embodied energy measurement techniques currently used in Switzerland and Germany.

The Swiss guidance used is from the document SIA D 0123 (SIA) and the German guidance used is from the guidance document Der oekologische Bauteilkatalog (BTK), each guidance produces a comparative method of determining the environmental impact of a construction material.

The guidelines measure environmental performance in different ways. THE SIA standard measures the construction/manufacturing environmental and renewal impact in CO_2 and SO_2 equivalents, the BTK guidelines measure green house effect, acidification and primary embodied energy in $KgCO_2$ and gSO_2 equivalent and Mj per m^2 respectively. Several roof constructions were considered, which are listed below.

Table A5.2 *Roof constructions considered for environmental performance*

No.	Roof type	Construction
1	Compact roof	Reinforced concrete deck with hot bitumen layer, foamed glass, two layers of poly bitumen, PE-foil and pebbles
2	Inverted warm roof	Reinforced concrete deck with two layers of poly bitumen, Polystyrol XPS filter fleece and pebbles
3	Warm roof	Reinforced concrete deck with bitumen vapour layer, Polystyrol (EPS), two layers of poly bitumen, PE-foil and pebbles
4	Warm roof	Reinforced concrete deck with bitumen vapour layer, Polystyrol (EPS), plastic waterproof layer, filter fleece and pebbles
5	Warm roof	Reinforced concrete deck with PE vapour layer, Polystyrol (EPS), plastic waterproof layer, filter fleece and pebbles
6	Warm roof	Wooden deck with bitumen vapour layer, Polystyrol (EPS), two layers of poly bitumen, PE-foil and pebbles
7	Warm roof	Wooden deck with PE vapour layer, Polystyrol (EPS), plastic waterproof layer, filter fleece and pebbles
8	Cold roof	Plaster board, PE vapour layer, rock wool, wooden deck, filter fleece, plastic waterproof layer, filter fleece and pebbles
9	Cold roof	Plaster board, PE vapour layer, cellulose insulation, wooden deck, filter fleece, plastic waterproof layer, filter fleece and pebbles

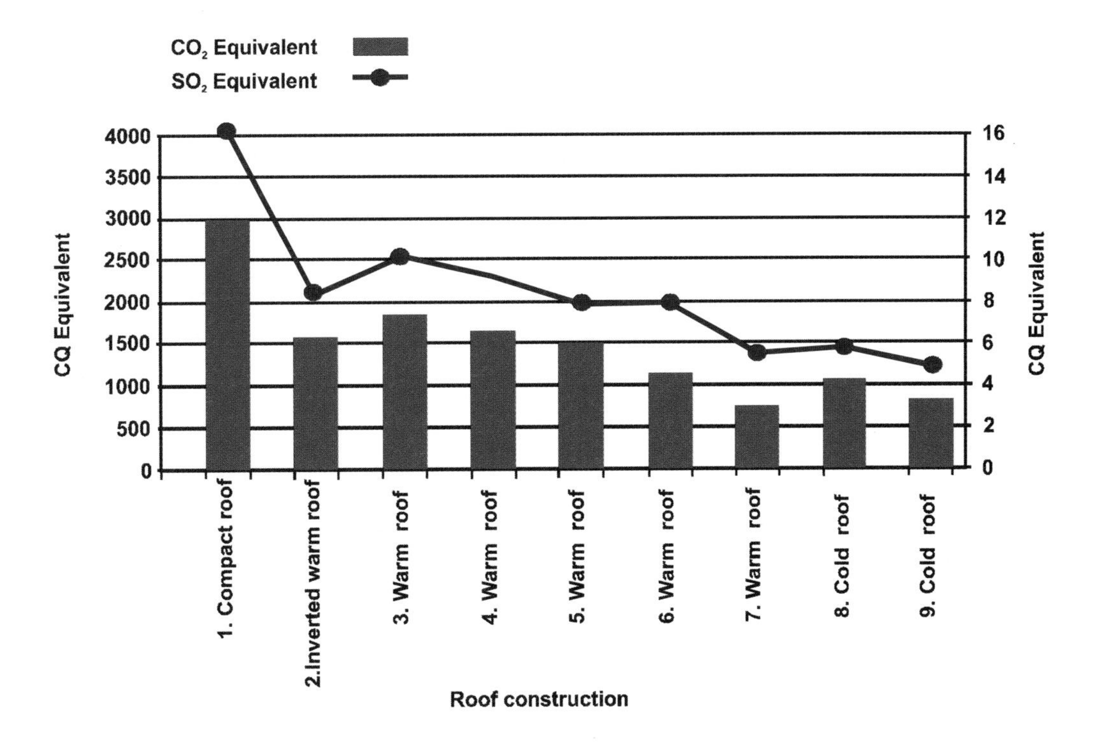

Figure A5.11 *SIA method greenhouse gas and acid rain results*

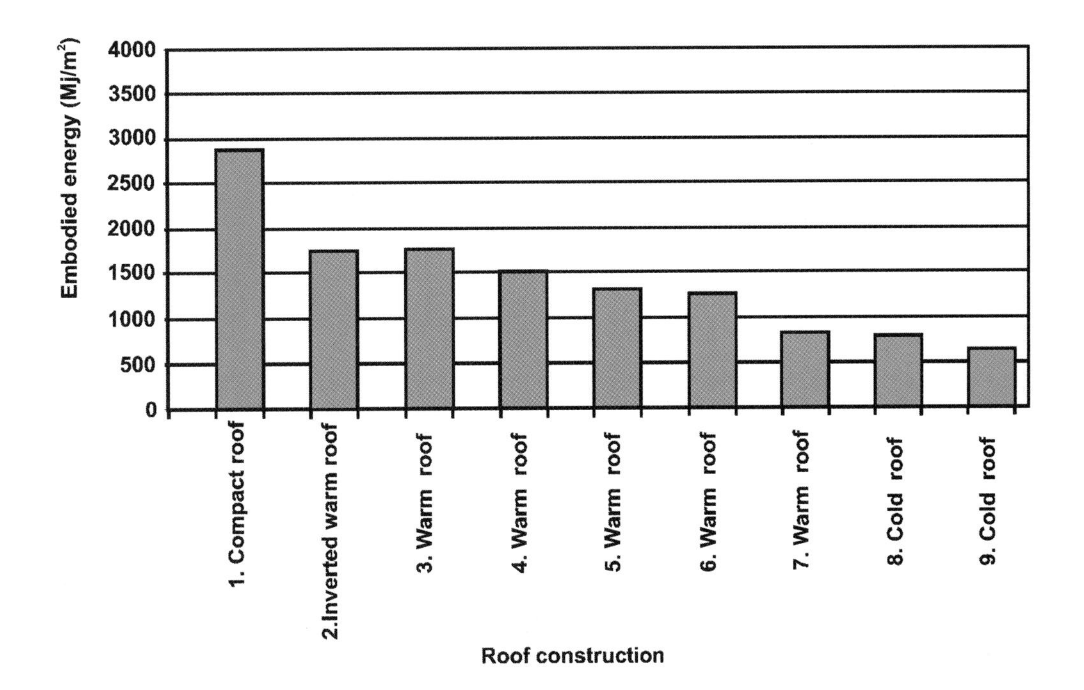

Figure A5.12 *BTK Embodied Energy results*

Both methodologies clearly show roof construction No.1 to have the highest environmental impact. They generally agree with the order of environmental impact for the other types of construction but the results differ in magnitude.

Processed materials have the highest environmental impact due to the energy required for manufacture. The highest environmental impact of any material is for foamed glass insulation followed by concrete for the compact roof construction. The waterproof layer has a high environmental impact per unit mass, but this is used sparingly.

The lowest environmental impact is for quarried stones despite their mass and for wood, which actually stores carbon and so has a negative score for greenhouse gas effect in the BTK system.

Although this study only considered standard roof construction without the green roof substrate and drainage layers, it still shows an important trend of greater environmental impact for processed and manufactured components than for non-processed materials.

This study is directly applicable to the green roof materials and construction techniques used.

GLOSSARY

Albedo	A measure of how reflective a surface is. The albedo of a surface is the fraction of light that is reflected by an object (an albedo of 0 means that the surface absorbs all light and an albedo of 1 means that all light is reflected).
Antecedent conditions	The conditions prevailing prior to a rainfall event.
Attenuation	In the context of stormwater management, this is the process of reducing the peak flow and increasing the duration of a flow event.
Balancing pond	A pond designed to attenuate flows by storing runoff during the peak flow and releasing it at a controlled rate during and after the peak flow has passed. The pond always contains water (also known as wet detention pond).
Biocide	A natural or synthetic substance toxic to living organisms.
Biodegradation	Decomposition of matter by micro-organisms and other living things.
Biodiversity	The variety of life on earth. This means species, genetic variations within species, and the communities, habitats and ecosystems within which they occur.
Bioshading	The use of vegetation to shade windows and other glazed areas in order to control the amount of solar radiation entering a building.
Birds of conservation concern	A document, drawn up by governmental and non-governmental organisations, listing birds whose UK populations are declining and/or considered to be under threat <www.bto.org/psob/index.htm> (accessed 2007).
Brown roof	A green roof where the vegetation is intended to replicate brownfield habitat. It can be seeded or self colonised.
Burnt Clay	An alternative term for ceramic roof tiles. Crushed ceramic tiles can be used as a drainage layer on green roofs.
Carrying capacity	The maximum number of organisms or amount of biomass that can be supported in a given area.
Catchment	The area contributing surface water flow to a point on a drainage or river system. The catchment can be divided into sub-catchments.
Climax community	The final stage of ecological succession where a community reaches a state of equilibrium with its environment.
Community	Any group of populations of different organisms living together in the same locality. The community is the biological component of an ecosystem.
Conduction	The transmission of energy through a substance from a high energy region to a lower energy region, eg the transmission of heat from a hot region to a cool region.
Conservation	A series of measures required to maintain or restore natural habitats and populations of species of wild fauna and flora.
Convection	The circulatory motion in a liquid or gas, resulting from the tendency of hotter, less dense fluids to rise and colder, denser material to sink.

Diffuse pollution	Pollution arising from land-use activities (urban and rural) that are dispersed across a catchment, or sub-catchment, and do not arise as a process effluent, municipal sewage effluent, or an effluent discharge from farm buildings.
Disturbance	Disruption of natural process or behaviour.
Ecology	The scientific study of the inter-relationships among and between organisms, and between them and all aspects, living and non-living, of their environment.
Ecosystem	An ecological system of any scale, consisting of communities of organisms interacting with their environment.
Energy balance	A systematic presentation of energy flows and transformations in a system.
Environmental impact assessment (EIA)	The procedure, required to get planning permission for some new developments, for ensuring that the likely effects of the development on the environment are fully understood and taken into account before it goes ahead.
Ephemeral	Short lived or of brief duration.
Eutrophication	The process by which nutrients are accumulated in a water body, with a consequent growth of algae.
Evapotranspiration	The combined process of evaporation of water and transpiration from plants.
Expanded clay or slate	A material produced by firing clay in a kiln at a very high temperature. As it is fired, the organic compounds in the clay burn off forcing it to expand and become honeycombed while the outside surface is sintered. This produces ceramic pellets that are lightweight, porous and have a high strength.
Extensive green roof	A roof with thin soil, and little or no irrigation, which creates stressful ie low water retention and nutrient poor, conditions for plants.
Fauna	Term used to describe the animal life of a particular place, region or period of time.
Field capacity	Soil is at its field capacity when all the water that can has drained from a soil by gravity.
Filtration	The act of removing sediment or other particles from a fluid by passing it through a filter.
Flora	Term used to describe the plant life of a particular place, region or period of time.
Foam tiles	Rigid foam boards with grooves or deformations on one side to allow drainage. Used in drainage layer of green roofs.
Foamed glass	A lightweight, fine pored, expanded glass material produced from waste glass. Used as a lightweight bulk fill, drainage material and insulation in civil engineering and building applications.
Geocomposite	A combination of two geosynthetic materials used to form a drainage layer. Typically comprise a hard plastic core with a geotextile bonded to one or both sides. The core can be a geonet or a profiled sheet.
Geonet	A three dimensional regular grid structure of polymeric material formed by joined intersecting ribs. The parallel arrays of ribs intersect each other to form diamond shaped apertures. One array sits on top of the other to form a grid that has a depth of between 510 mm. Used as drainage layers.

Geotextile	A plastic fabric that is permeable.
Grassland	Ground covered by vegetation that is dominated by grasses.
Greenfield site	A site that is covered by vegetation and has never been developed except for agricultural or similar use.
Greenfield runoff	This is the surface water runoff from a site prior to development.
Green roof	A green roof is one with plants intentionally growing on its surface. The vegetated surface provides a degree of retention, attenuation and treatment of rainwater, and promotes evapotranspiration (depending on construction details, also known as an eco roof, roof garden, living roof or brown/ rubble roof).
Habitat	The place where an organism lives, often defined on the basis of uniformity of vegetation (woodland, reedbed etc).
Habitat mosaic	An area characterised by two or more types of habitat that are arranged as a mosaic of a number of small areas of each habitat type.
Higher plant	Plants which have vascular tissue forming channels for conducting water and nutrients, as opposed to lower plants, such as mosses, liverworts etc which do not.
Hydroseeding	The process by which a water based solution, which includes plant seeds and a variety of chemicals to encourage their rapid growth, is sprayed onto surfaces, including those that are nearly vertical, to provide a layer of vegetation.
Hydromulching	A development of hydroseeding where mulch is added to the mixture that is sprayed onto surfaces to improve the ability of the seed to remain in place.
Indigenous	An indigenous organism is one that is native to a particular place.
Infiltration capacity	The maximum rate at which the soil can absorb falling rain or melting snow.
Interception storage	Storage of water in a drainage system so that runoff does not occur from a site up to the first 5 mm of rainfall.
Intensive green roof	A roof with deep soil, irrigation systems, and fertile conditions for plants.
Invertebrate	An animal without a backbone, including insects and spiders.
Inverted roof	A roof where the insulation is provided over the top of the waterproofing membrane.
Latent heat	The heat released or absorbed by a substance during a phase change, eg from a liquid to a gas.
Lower plants	Non vascular plants, ie mosses and fungi.
Maximum water capacity	The water content of a substance after being completely saturated and then allowed to drain for two hours (FLL 2002 definition).
Mitigation	Measures taken to reduce adverse impacts.
Mulch	Any loose material placed over the soil to control weeds and conserve soil moisture.
Permeability	A measure of the ease with which a fluid can flow through a porous medium. It depends on the physical properties of the medium, for example, the grain size, porosity and pore shape of soil.
Photosynthesis	The process in green plants and certain other organisms by which organic compounds are synthesised from carbon dioxide and water using light as an energy source. Most forms of photosynthesis release oxygen as a by-product.

Pollution	A change in the physical, chemical, radiological or biological quality of a resource (air, water or land) caused by man or man's activities, which is injurious to existing, intended or potential uses of the resource.
Population	A group comprising the same species present in the same locality.
Protected species	Certain plant or animal species that are protected to various degrees in law, particularly by the Wildlife and Countryside Act 1981 (as amended).
Solar radiation	Energy from the sun. Also known as short-wave radiation. Of importance to the climate system, solar radiation includes ultraviolet radiation, visible radiation, and infrared radiation.
Rainwater harvesting rainwater use system	A system that collects rainwater from where it falls rather than or allowing it to drain away, and includes water that is collected within the boundaries of a property, from roofs and surrounding surfaces.
Red data book species	These are lists of species whose continued existence is threatened. Red data book species are classified into different categories of perceived risk. Each red data book usually deals with a specific group of animals or plants (for instance, reptiles, insects or mosses). They are now being published in many different countries. The Joint Nature Conservation Committee is responsible for some of these publications reflecting the status of some plant species types in the UK and Ireland.
Ruderal	A ruderal plant is one that colonises waste ground or that is associated with human dwellings or agriculture.
Runoff	Water flow over the surface to the drainage system. This occurs if the ground is impermeable, is saturated or if rainfall is particularly intense.
Runoff coefficient	Percentage of rainfall that turns into surface water running off the roof.
Sensible heat	Heat that is transported by a body, which has a temperature higher than its surroundings, via conduction, convection, or both.
Simple intensive roof	A roof with a soil layer that is thicker than an extensive roof green but thinner than an intensive roof. The plants used require less irrigation and fertilisation than those on an intensive green roof.
Species	A group of organisms that resemble each other closely and can interbreed within the group but cannot exchange genes with other groups.
Source control	The control of runoff at or near its source.
Substrate	Any object or material upon which an organism grows or is attached.
Succession	The process of ecological communities developing from one type to another.
SUDS	Sustainable drainage systems or sustainable (urban) drainage systems. A sequence of management practices and control structures designed to drain surface water in a more sustainable fashion than some conventional techniques (may also be referred to as SUDS).
Surface water management train	The management of runoff in stages as it drains from a site.
Suspended solids	Undissolved particles in a liquid.
Thermal mass	The amount of potential heat storage capacity available.

Time of concentration	Time taken for rainwater to flow from the remotest part of the catchment area to the point under consideration.
Time of entry	Time taken for rainwater to reach an inlet into the drainage system after hitting the ground.
Translocation	The physical removal of either an area of habitat or a number of individuals of a certain species from one site (the donor site) to another (the receptor site).
Treatment	Improving the quality of water by physical, chemical and/or biological means.
Turbidity	Reduced transparency of a liquid caused by the presence of undissolved matter.
Wildlife	Any undomesticated organism.
Xeric	A dry, as opposed to a wet (hydric) or intermediate (mesic), environment

ABBREVIATIONS

BAP	Biodiversity action plan
CDM	Construction (Design and Management) Regulations
CIRIA	Construction Industry Research and Information Association
CRoW	Countryside Rights of Way Act 2000
Defra	Department of Environment Food and Rural Affairs
DCLG	Department of Communities and Local Government
EA	Environment Agency
FEH	Flood Estimation Handbook
FLL	Forschungsgesellschaft Landschaftsentwicklung Landschaftsbau e.V
FSR	Flood studies report
GLA	Greater London Authority
ICoP	Interim Code of Practice
LDD	Local development documents
LDF	Local development framework
NAW	National Assembly for Wales
NDC	New deal for communities
NSWG	National SUDS Working Group
ODPM	Office of the Deputy Prime Minster
PPG	Planning policy guidance
PPS	Planning policy statement
PV	Photovoltaics
RSS	Regional spatial strategy
SPD	Supplementary planning document
SPG	Supplementary planning guidance
SUDS	Sustainable drainage systems
SSSI	Site of special scientific interest
TAN15	Technical Advice Note (Wales) 15 Development and flood risk
TCPA	Town and Country Planning Act 1990
TSS	Total suspended solids
UDP	Unitary development plan
UV	Ultraviolet
WCA	Wildlife and Countryside Act 1981
WFD	Water Framework Directive (2000/06/EC)
WLC	Whole life costing

REFERENCES

Allaby, M (1998)
Dictionary of Ecology (3rd edition)
Oxford University Press (ISBN-13: 978-019860-905-6)

American Wick Drain Corporation (undated)
Roof Garden Components
< http://www.americanwick.com/products/product_cat_detail.cfm?prod_cat_id=9 >

American Wick Drain Corporation (undated a)
Comparing the AMERGREEN Prefabricated drainage material to sand and gravel
http://www.americanwick.com/products/product_cat_detail.cfm?prod_cat_id=9

Anon (2003)
Green Roofs
Research Advice Note, British Council for Offices

Ashamawy, A K (2004)
The hanging gardens of Babylon
<http://ce.eng.usf.edu/pharos/wonders/gardens.html>

Auckland Regional Council (2003)
Stormwater management devices, design guidelines manual (2nd edition)
Auckland Regional Council

Banting, D, Doshi, H, Li, J and Missios, P (2005)
Report on the environmental benefits and costs of green roof technology for the City of Toronto
Prepared for City of Toronto and Ontario Centres of Excellence – Earth and Environmental Technologies. Ryerson University <http://www.toronto.ca/greenroofs/pdf/executivesummary.pdf >

Bodsworth, E, Shepherd, P and Plant, C (2005)
Exotic plant species on brownfield land and their value to invertebrates of nature conservation importance
English Nature Research Report No.650
<http://www.english-nature.org.uk/pubs/publication/
Pub_Results.asp?PageNo=119&C=3&K=&I=&A=&k2=>

Boscoe, A (2003)
An assessment of green roofs to act as mitigation tool increased urban densities
Livingroofs.organisation, <http://www.livingroofs.org/NewFiles/DissertgreenroofAboscoe.pdf>

Brenneisen, S (2001)
Vogel, Kafer und Spinnen auf Dachbegrunungen – Nutzungsmoglichkeiten und Einrichtungsoptimeierungen
Geographisches Institut Universitat (University of Basel). Basel/ Baudepartment des Kantons Basel-Stadt

Brenneisen,S (2003)
"The benefits of biodiversity from green roofs – key design consequences"
In: *Proc 1st annual conf Greening roof tops for sustainable communities, Chicago*, 29-30 May 2003.
University of Applied Sciences, Wadenswil, Switzerland

Brenneisen, S (2004)
"From biodiversity strategies to agricultural productivity"
In: *Proc 2nd annual conf Greening roof tops for sustainable communities, Portland*, 24 June 2004, University of Applied Sciences, Wadenswil, Switzerland

British Council for Offices (2003)
Green roofs
Research advice note, published jointly with Corporation of London. BCO, London <http://www.bco.org.uk/research/researchreports/detail.cfm?rid=45&cid=0>

Brown, R, D and Gillespie, T, J (1995)
Microclimatic Landscape Design: Creating Thermal Comfort and Energy Efficiency
John Wiley and Sons (ISBN-13: 978-0471056676)

IHS (2004)
Reducing the effects of climate change by roof design
BRE Digest 486, 2004, BRE (ISBN 1 86081 692 4)

Burgess H (2004)
An assessment of the potential of green roofs for bird conservation in the UK
Livingroofs.org <http://www.livingroofs.org/images/BirdsOnRoofs.pdf>

Burton R M (1983)
Flora of the London area
London Natural History Society, London <http://www.lnhs.org.uk/history.htm>

City of Portland Environmental Services (2002)
Stormwater management manual
September 2002, Revision 3 <http://www.portlandonline.com/shared/cfm/image.cfm?id=55746>

City of Westminster (2003)
Supplementary planning guidance on sustainable building
Westminster City Council working in partnership with Entec UK Limited

Coppin, N, J and Richards, I, G (1990)
Use of vegetation in civil engineering
CIRIA/Butterworths, B10, London

Concern for Swifts (2002)
<www.concernforswifts.com/index.html>

Corporation of London (2003)
Biodiversity action plan

DCLG (2006)
Planning Policy Statements (PPS) 3: Housing
HMSO, London

DCLG (2006)
Planning policy Statement (PPS) 25: Development and flood risk
HMSO, London

DCLG (2007)
Development and Flood Risk: A Practice Guide Companion to PPS25
"Living Draft – A Consultation Paper" London, 2007

DEFRA (2002)
Working with the grain of nature. A biodiversity strategy for England

DEFRA (2005)
Securing the future
UK Government sustainable development strategy

Department of the Environment (1994)
Biodiversity the UK action plan
HMSO, January 1994

DETR (2000)
Building a Better Quality of Life – A strategy for more sustainable construction.

Dewar, S, M and Shawyer, C, R (2001)
Boxes, Baskets and Platforms – artificial nest sites for owls and other birds of prey
The Hawk and Owl Trust, Taunton

DiCorcia, D (2002)
A guide to Frank Lloyd Wright's Falling Water
<http://me.essortment.com/franklloydwr_rcwb.htm>

Dunnett, N (2006)
"Green Roofs for Biodiversity: Reconciling Aesthetics with Ecology"
In: *Proc 4th annual conf Greening roof tops for sustainable communities, Boston*, 10–12 May 2006

Dunnett, N and Kingsbury, N (2004)
Planting Green Roofs and Living Walls
Timber Press (ISBN: 0-88192-640-X)

Dunnett, N, Nagase, A, Booth, R and Grime, P (2005)
"Vegetation composition and structure significantly influence green roof performance"
In: *Proc 2nd Int Conf Greening roof tops for sustainable communities, Washington DC*, 4–6 May 2005

Earth Pledge Foundation, Hoffman, L and McDonough W (2005)
Green Roofs – Ecological Design and Construction
Schiffer Publishing (ISBN-13: 978-076432-189-4)

Ernst, W (2003)
Dachabdichtung Dachbegruenung, Sonerband Abdichtung
Fraunhofer IRB Verlag, (ISBN: 3-81676-326-X)

Frerichs, E (2002)
"Green roofs help to protect salmon habitat in Portland"
The green roof infrastructure monitor Volume 4, No1, Green roofs for Healthy Cities
<http://www.greenroofs.org/resources/GRIM-Winter2002.pdf>

Frith, M and Gedge, D (2000)
The black redstart in urban Britain; a conservation conundrum?
British Wildlife, 11, 381–388

Frith, M and Gedge, D (2004)
"Integer, Diggers and Bedzed" Green Roofs for British Housing
In: Proc 2nd annual conf Greening roof tops for sustainable communities, Portland, 24 June 2004

FLL (2000)
Richtlinie fuer die Planung, Ausfuehrung und Pflege von Fassadenbegruenungen mit Kletterplanzen Forschungsgesellschaft Landschaftsentwicklung Landschaftsbau e.V (FLL) (ISBN: 3-93448-450-6)

FFL (2002)
Guidelines for planning, execution and upkeep of green roof sites
Research Association for Landscape Development and Landscape Construction, Forschungsgesellschaft Landschaftsentwicklung Landschaftsbau e.V, (FLL), Release 2002 (English version), Germany Funktionen und Wirkungen der Dachbegrünung, Hochschule für Technik Rapperswil, Abteilung Landschaftsarchitektur, <http://www.hsr.ch/Landschaftsarchitektur>

Gaffin, S (2005)
Energy Balance Applied to a Comparison of White and Green Roof Cooling Efficiency
Centre for Climate Research, Columbia University & Penn State Centre for Green Roof Research, Penn State University, USA. In: Proc 2nd Int Conf Greening roof tops for sustainable communities, Washington DC, 46 May 2005

Gedge, D (2003)
"From rubble to redstarts"
In: *Proc 1st annual conf Greening roof tops for sustainable communities, Chicago*, 29-30 May 2003

Gedge, D and Kadas, G (2004)
"Bugs, Bees and Spiders:green roof design for rare invertebrates"
In: *Proc 2nd annual conf Greening roof tops for sustainable communities, Portland*, 2–4 June 2004

Gedge, D and Kadas, G (2005)
"Green roofs for biodiversity: Designing green roofs to meet targets of BAP (biodiversity action plan) species"
In: *Proc int conf World Green Roof Congress, Basel, Switzerland,* 15-16 September 2005

Gibson C W D (1998)
Brownfield: red data. The values artificial habitats have for uncommon invertebrates
English Nature Research Report No. 273. Peterborough, UK

Gilbert O (1990)
The Lichen Flora of Urban Wasteland
Lichenologist 22: 87-101 Part 1

GLA (2002)
The Mayor's Biodiversity Strategy – connecting with London's nature
Greater London Authority, July 2002

Grant, G, Engleback, L and Nicholson, B (2003)
Green roofs: their existing status and potential for conserving biodiversity in urban areas
English Nature Research Report. Report No 498 <http://www.english-nature.co.uk/news/news_photo/Greenroofs.pdf>

Greenroof.com
Components
<www.greenroofs.com> 14 January 2002

GreenTech (undated)
Green Roofs/Roof Gardens Systems
<http://www.greentechitm.com/systems/roof.asp>

Hampshire Bat Group (2006)
Bat Droppings
Newsletter of the Hampshire Bat Group, Spring 2006,
<http://www.hants.gov.uk/bats/docs/Bat_Droppings_Spring06.pdf>

Harrison, H, W (2000)
Roofs and Roofing
Building Research Establishment, CRC Ltd (ISBN: 1 86081 068 3)

Harvey, P (2001)
The East Thames Corridor; a nationally important invertebrate fauna under threat
British Wildlife, 12, 91–98

Herman, R (2003)
"Green Roofs in Germany: Yesterday, Today and Tomorrow"
In: *Proc 1st annual conf Greening roof tops for sustainable communities, Chicago*, 29-30 May 2003

Hewlett (2002)
The breeding birds of the London Area

The roof gardens (undated)
History of The Roof Gardens, Babylon
<http://www.roofgardens.com/introduction/history/> Accessed 2 June 2006

HSE (1998)
HSG 33 – Heath and safety in roofwork
HMSO (ISBN: 0-71761-425-5)

Heisler, G, M et al (1995)
"Urban Forests – Cooling Our Communities, , Inside Urban Eco Systems"
In: *Proc 7th National Urban Forest Conference, American Forests*, 12-16 September 1995

Hendy, J (1997)
Balconies and Roof Gardens
New Holland, London

Ingleby, A (2002)
Green Roofs: A study of their benefits and barriers to installation in London
Livingroofs.org

International Council on Monuments and Sites (2005)
Heritage at Risk – Iceland
<http://www.international.icomos.org/risk/icela_2000.htm>

Howe, J (accessed 2007)
Le Corbusier Villa Savoye
http://www.bc.edu/bc_org/avp/cas/fnart/Corbu.html

Hurstwic (2006)
Hurstwic
<http://www.hurstwic.org/history/articles/daily_living/text/Turf_Houses.htm>

Japan Association for the 2005 World Exposition (2005)
The concept of bio lung
<http://www.expo2005.or.jp/en/venue/biolung.html>

Jenric K (2005)
Green roofs – A horticultural perspective
Livingroofs.org

Johnston, C, McCreary, K and Nelms, C (2003)
"Vancouver Public Library green roof monitoring project"
In: *Proc 1st annual conf Greening roof tops for sustainable communities, Chicago*, 29-30 May 2003

Johnston, J and Newton, J (2004)
Building Green, a guide to using plants on roofs, walls and pavements
Greater London Authority, May 2004 (ISBN: 1-85261-637-7)

Jones, R (2002)
Tecticolous invertebrates. A preliminary investigation of the invertebrate fauna on ecoroofs in urban London
English Nature

Kadas, G (2002)
Study of invertebrates on green roofs – how roof design can maximise biodiversity in an urban environment
University College London, unpublished

Keeley, M (2005)
Green roofs and green area factor: an urban-green infrastructure policy instrument
In: *Proc 2nd Int Conf Greening roof tops for sustainable communities, Washington DC*, 4–6 May 2005

Kellagher, R and Lauchlan, C, S (2005)
Use of SUDS in high density developments, Guidance Manual
HR Wallingford Report SR666, Release 3.0, June 2005

Köhler, M (1993)
Fassaden und Dachbegruenung
Ulmer

Koehler, M and Schmidt, M (2002)
Das Mikroklima extensiver Gruendaecher
FLL Jahrbuch 2002– Dachbegruennung, Thalacker Medien (ISBN: 3 87815 179 9)

Koehler, M and Schmidt, M (2002a)
"Photvoltaik-Panels on Greened Roofs, Positive Interaction between two elements of sustainable architecture" *RIO 02, World Climate and Energy Event, Rio de Janeiro* (ISBN: 8 59027 101 3
<http://www.rio02.de/proceedings/pdf/151_Koehler.pdf>

Kohler, M and Schmidt, M (2003)
Study of extensive "green roofs" in Berlin
<www.roofmeadow.com> page downloaded 5/8/05. Translation of Koehler Manfred and Schmidt Marco (2001.) Long-term Studies on Green Roofs in Berlin - Part 3 - Substance retention . Dach und Grün

Koehler, M (2004)
"Energetic effects of green roofs to the urban climate near to the ground and to the building surfaces"
In: *Proc Int Green Roof congress, Nurtingen*, Sept 2004

Koehler, M (2005)
Dach und Gruen
Sept 2005 (ISSN: 0943 5271)

Kolb, W and Schwarz, T (1999)
Dachbegrunung, Intensiv und extensive
Ulmer (ISBN: 3-80015-075-1)

Kolb, W (2002)
Wenn Regen auf das Gruendach Faellt
Jahrbuch Dachbegruennung 2002, Bundersverband Garten-, Landschafts- und Sportzplatzbau E.V., Thalaker Medien (ISBN: 3-87815-179-9)

Krauter, S and Ochs, F (2002)
An all-in-one solar home system
In: *Proc 29th IEEE Photovoltaic Specialists Conference, Rio de Janeiro, Brazil*, 1924 May 2002 pp 1668 – 1671 (ISBN: 8-59027-101-3)
<http://ieeexplore.ieee.org/xpl/freeabs_all.jsp?tp=&arnumber=1190938&isnumber=26685>

LaBerge, K, Worthington, K, Mulvaney, P, Bolliger, R (2005)
"City of Chicago green roof test plot study: Stormwater and temperature results"
In: *Proc 2nd Int Conf Greening roof tops for sustainable communities, Washington DC*, 4–6 May 2005

Le Corbusier
History of Architecture
<http://www.stclairc.on.ca/people/pages/fperissi/arc300ge/week10/lecorbu.html>

Leggett, D, Brown, R, Brewer, D, Stanfield, G, and Holliday, E (2001)
Rainwater and greywater use in buildings: Best practice guidance
C539, CIRIA, London

Liptan, T and Strecker, E (2003)
"Ecoroofs (Greenroofs) – A more sustainable infrastructure"
In: *Proc Nat Conf on Urban Stormwater: Enhancing Programs at the Local Level*, United States Environmental Protection Agency. February 17-20, 2003.

Liptan, T Miller, T and Roy, A (2004)
"Portland Ecoroof Vision: Quantitative study to support policy decisions"
In: *Proc 2nd annual conf Greening roof tops for sustainable communities, Portland*, 24 June 2004

Livingston, E, H, Miller, C, and Lohr, M (2004)
"Green roof design and implementation in Florida"
In: *Proc 2nd annual conf Greening roof tops for sustainable communities, Portland,* 24 June 2004

LBAP 2006
Lancashire biodiversity action plan
<http://www.lbap.co.uk/>

LBP 2006
London Biodiversity Action Plan
London Biodiversity Partnership <http://www.lbp.org.uk/>

London Borough of Lewisham (2002)
Revised Unitary Development Plan
<www2.lewisham.gov.uk/lbl/planning/udp/foreword.html>

Lui, K and Boivin, M, A (2002)
"NRC's Institute for research in construction studying plant survivability and stormwater management in Ottowa"
Green Roof Infrastructure Monitor, Vol 4, No 1 2002

Lui, K and Minor, J (2005)
"Performance evaluation of an extensive green roof"
In: *Proc 2nd Int Conf Greening roof tops for sustainable communities, Washington DC*, 4–6 May 2005

Lundberg, L (2005)
"Swedish Research on green roofs and information outreach"
In: *Proc 2nd Int Conf Greening roof tops for sustainable communities, Washington DC*, 4–6 May 2005

Macmillan, G (2003)
"York University rooftop garden stormwater quantity and quality performance monitoring report"
In: *Proc 1st annual conf Greening roof tops for sustainable communities, Chicago*, 29-30 May 2003

Mentens, J, Raes, D and Hermy, M (2003)
"Effect of orientation on the water balance of green roofs"
In: *Proc 1st annual conf Greening roof tops for sustainable communities, Chicago*, 29-30 May 2003

Miller, C (2006)
Use of vegetated roof covers in runoff management
Roofscapes Inc

Miller, C (2006a)
Green roofs as stormwater best management practices, Evaluation of the effective green roof perviousness, Sample analysis, mid atlantic states
Roofscapes Inc

Mitchell-Jones, A, J (2004)
Bat Mitigation Guidelines
English Nature

Moller, M (2005)
Green Roofs and their Potential as a Habitat for Bryophytes in Central London
Dissertation for Master of Environmental Science, Kingston University, 2005

Moran, A, Hunt, B, and Smith, J (2005)
"Hydrologic and water quality performance from green roofs in Goldsboro and Raleigh, North Carolina"
In: *Proc 2nd Int Conf Greening roof tops for sustainable communities, Washington DC*, 4–6 May 2005

Newcastle City Council (2001)
Your wildlife
Newcastle biodiversity action plan

Newton, J, Williams, C, Nicholson, B and Venables, R (2004)
Working with Wildlife – A training and resource pack for the construction industry
CIRIA C587, London

Ngan, G (2004)
Green Roof Policy: Tools for Encouraging Sustainable Design
British Columbia Society of Landscape Architects, BCSLA, Canada

Norfolk Bat Group (2003)
Bats and bat boxes
<www.norfolk-bat-group.org.uk/framebb.html>

ODPM (2005)
Making it happen in neighbourhoods, the national strategy for neighbourhood renewal – four years on
Office of the Deputy Prime Minister, Neighbourhood renewal unit

ODPM (2005)
Planning Policy Statement (PPS) 1: *Delivering sustainable development*
HMSO, London

ODPM (2005)
Planning Policy Statement (PPS) 9: *Biodiversity and geological conservation*
HMSO, London

ODPM (2005)
Planning Policy Statement (PPS) 11*: Regional Spatial Strategies*
HMSO, London

ODPM (2006)
Planning for biodiversity and geological conservation – A guide to good practice
HMSO, London

Payne, R (2000)
The Flora of Roofs
King's Lynn Privately Published

Pearsall, J (2001)
The New Oxford Dictionary of English
Oxford University Press

Peck, S, W, Callaghan, C, Kuhn, M, E and Bass, B (1999)
Greenbacks from green roofs: forging an new industry in Canada
Canada Mortgage and Housing Corporation

Peck Associates (undated)
Public benefits of green roofs
Green Roofs For Healthy Cities, Peck Associates, <http://www.cardinalgroup.ca/grhcc/public.htm>

Pennsylvania Department of Environmental Protection (2004)
Draft stormwater Best Management Practices Manual
Harrisburg PA, December 2004

Roberts, S (1991)
Solar Electricity, A practical guide to designing and installing small photovoltaic systems
Prentice Hall, Int Ed (ISBN: 0-13826-314-0)

Roofscapes Inc (200)
Mathematical simulation methods. A foundation for developing a general purpose green roof simulation model
Philadelphia

Roofscapes Inc (2002)
Use of vegetated roof covers in runoff management
Technical Note 9 July 2002. Philadelphia

Royal Horticultural Society (RHS) (2001)
Plants for Places
Royal Horticultural Society, Dorian Kindersely Limited (ISBN: 1 4053 0738)

Santamouris, M (2001)
P7, Energy and Climate in the Urban Built Environment
M Santamouris (ed), James and James (Science Publishers) Ltd (ISBN: 1-87393-690-7)

Scottish Natural Heritage (2003)
Bats in Buildings, A guide for building professionals
Scottish Natural Heritage, English Nature, Environment and Heritage Service, Countryside Council for Wales, Health and Safety Executive, Bat Conservation Trust, DEFRA, <http://www.snh.org.uk/pdfs/species/BatsBuildings.pdf>

Semrad, G (2004)
Hundertwasser Kunstbauwerke on Oesterreich
HB (ISBN: 3-95004-511-2)

Simpson and Brown Architects (1996)
The Design and Construction of Bat Boxes in Houses
Scottish Natural Heritage, Perth.

Southern Water (2006)
Biodiversity
Southern Water website
<http://www.southernwater.co.uk/educationandenvironment/biodiversityactionplan/explorer/habitats/grassland.asp>

Strahler, A and Strahler, A (2002)
Physical Geography, Science and systems of the Human Environment
2nd edition, Wiley (ISBN: 0-47123-800-7)

Takenaka Corporation (Accessed July 2007)
High Rise Large Scale Stepped Roof Greening Technology
Takenaka Corporation <http://www.takenaka.co.jp/takenaka_e/env_pro_e/09_across/02.htm>

Takenaka Corporation (2001)
Heat Island Phenomenon Proven to Be Alleviated by Rooftop Greening
Updated, Takenaka Corporation,
<http://www.takenaka.co.jp/takenaka_e/news_e/pr0108/m0108_05.htm>

Tarr, A (2002)
"Design and performance of planted roof systems and their potential within SUDS developments"
In: *Proc standing conf. on Stormwater Source Control, Volume XXIII, Coventry University*

Toronto City Council (2006)
Making green roofs happen
Consolidated clause in Policy and Finance Committee Report 1. Considered by City Council on 31 January and 1-2 February, 2006. Toronto City Council, City Clerk
<http://www.toronto.ca/greenroofs/policy.htm>

United States Environmental Protection Agency (2000)
Vegetated roof cover
Philadelphia, Pennsylvania Office of water, Report EPA-841-B-00-005D,
<http://www.epa.gov/nps/roofcover.pdf>

Water Works UK (2006)
<www.wwuk.co.uk>

Westminster City Council (2003)
Westminster City's sustainable building supplementary planning guidance
<http://www.westminster.gov.uk/environment/planning/sitesandprojectspolicies/upload/28823_1.pdf>

Woods-Ballard, B, Kellagher, R, Martin, P, Jefferies, C, Bray, R, and Shaffer, P (2006)
The SUDS Manual
C697, CIRIA, London

The Wildlife Trust for Birmingham and the Black Country (2000)
Birmingham and the Black Country biodiversity action plan
<http://www.wildlifetrust.org.uk/urbanwt/ecorecord/bap/html/main.htm>

Yannas, S, Erell, E and Molina, J, L (2006)
Roof Cooling Techniques – A Design Handbook
X330, Earthscan (ISBN: 1-84407-313-0)